INSTITUTE OF PSYCHIATRY

*Maudsley Monographs*

# CHILDREN OF SICK PARENTS
## AN ENVIRONMENTAL AND PSYCHIATRIC STUDY

INSTITUTE OF PSYCHIATRY

MAUDSLEY MONOGRAPHS

*Number Sixteen*

---

# CHILDREN OF SICK PARENTS

## AN ENVIRONMENTAL
## AND PSYCHIATRIC STUDY

*By*

MICHAEL RUTTER, M.D., M.R.C.P., D.P.M.

*Senior Lecturer, Institute of Psychiatry,*
*The Maudsley Hospital, London*

LONDON
OXFORD UNIVERSITY PRESS
NEW YORK    TORONTO
1966

*Oxford University Press, Ely House, London W.1*

GLASGOW NEW YORK TORONTO MELBOURNE WELLINGTON
CAPE TOWN SALISBURY IBADAN NAIROBI LUSAKA ADDIS ABABA
BOMBAY CALCUTTA MADRAS KARACHI LAHORE DACCA
KUALA LUMPUR HONG KONG

PRINTED IN GREAT BRITAIN

# CONTENTS

# MAUDSLEY MONOGRAPHS

HENRY MAUDSLEY, from whom this series of monographs takes its name, was the founder of The Maudsley Hospital and the most prominent English psychiatrist of his generation. The Maudsley Hospital is now united with Bethlem Royal Hospital, and its medical school, renamed the Institute of Psychiatry, has become part of the British Postgraduate Medical Federation. It is entrusted by the University of London with the duty to advance psychiatry by teaching and research.

The monograph series reports work carried out in the Institute and in the associated Hospital. Some of the monographs are directly concerned with clinical problems; others, less obviously relevant, are in scientific fields that are cultivated at the Institute because they provide knowledge and methods essential for the furtherance of psychiatry.

*Joint Editors*

# ACKNOWLEDGEMENTS

THIS book gives an account of work that formed the subject of an M.D. thesis submitted to the University of Birmingham. I am most grateful to Professor Sir Aubrey Lewis for advice on the planning of this study. My thanks are due also to the late Dr. Kenneth Cameron for permission to use the facilities of The Maudsley Hospital Children's Department, to other physicians of the Hospital for permission to study their patients, and to Professor R. Cocker for allowing me to interview the parents of children attending the Dental Department of King's College Hospital. Sir Wilfred Sheldon and Dr. Doyne Bell very kindly gave me permission to interview the parents of children attending their clinics at King's College Hospital and The Belgrave Hospital for Children. I am indebted to Dr. R. H. Cawley for advice on statistical matters. Mrs. Perkins and the Records Staff of The Maudsley Hospital gave much help in the tracing of records. I thank Dr. G. W. Brown and Dr. P. Graham for helpful comments on an earlier draft and Miss S. E. Hague for valuable criticisms and suggestions in drafting the final text. Finally, I thank Mrs. B. Hutton who did all the typing.

*London*                                                                    M. R.
*1965*

# INTRODUCTION

DEVIANT parental behaviour and attitudes (often attributed to psycho-pathology or mental illness) have long been regarded as aetiologically important for psychiatric disorders which begin in childhood, but the effects on the child of *overt* parental mental disorder and illness rather than of abnormal parental attitudes have been little studied. This is regrettable in the light of recent trends towards family therapy (Ackerman and Behrens, 1956; Ackerman, 1958; Bell, 1962; Dreikurs, 1951; Ehrenwald, 1963; Howells, 1963) and even the view that the child patient is only a sign of family psychopathology (Howells, 1962). Before establishing a concept of 'a sick child *ergo* a sick parent' it is necessary to know something of the associations between illnesses in parents and psychiatric disorders in their children. The present monograph is concerned with this basic problem.

The consequences for the family of illness in one member are clearly of great importance. Lewis (1956) stated: 'For the sociologist the family is a nuclear unit; for the anthropologist, bonds of kinship are of the first importance; and for the psychiatrist the family is the matrix within which the individual is moulded and developed, the area where his strongest emotional ties are formed, the background against which much of his most intense personal life is enacted. There is, therefore, need to study the family, not only from the psychoanalytical and psychological standpoint, but also to discover how mental illness impinges upon it, and what effects this sort of incapacity has on the family structure.' Illnesses, especially chronic illnesses, often bring about widespread and sometimes deleterious changes in the home. In this, chronic physical illness (Ekdahl *et al.*, 1962) and death have much in common with mental illness and the present investigation therefore extends to both physical and mental illnesses of parents.

Not only may a study of interactions between illnesses in the parent and the child improve understanding of the role of the environment in the aetiology of child psychiatric disorder, and of ways in which the family and social setting may determine the form of a disorder but there are also public health considerations. Treatment of adult illness involves decisions as to whether the patient should remain at home, be admitted to hospital or receive care elsewhere, and these must take into account not only what is best for the individual, but also the effects on the family. The effect upon children of a mentally ill parent in the home is particularly pertinent in view of recent trends towards community care of psychiatric patients.

Also, more may be learnt about fundamental connections between illness in childhood and subsequent adult psychiatric illness. Warren (1960) has emphasized the relevance of long-term follow-up inquiries. Studies of people treated years before for psychiatric disorders in childhood suggest that childish antisocial or conduct disorders may be related to adult criminality, sociopathic personality defects, or perhaps, even schizophrenia. On the other hand, children with neurotic disturbances often become normal adults (Morris *et al.*, 1954; Morris *et al.*, 1956; O'Neal and Robins, 1958, 1959; O'Neal *et al.*, 1960).

Longitudinal behavioural studies from early infancy have shown the relevance of temperamental characteristics (Chess *et al.*, 1963; Rutter *et al.*, 1964; Thomas *et al.*, 1963) which are in part genetically determined (Rutter *et al.*, 1963). Twin studies have demonstrated the role of heredity in child psychiatric disorder (Shields, 1954) and emphasized the interaction between genetic endowment and environmental variables (Rutter *et al.*, 1963). It is not known whether such factors are identical with those which play a part in the aetiology of psychiatric disorders of adults, and the fact that children who have had psychiatric illness are more likely to have psychiatric illness in adult life does not necessarily imply homogeneity of childhood and adult psychiatric illness. Nevertheless, the aetiological relationship between illness in the child and in the adult is important for the understanding of both.

Epidemiological studies can reveal associations between illnesses in different members of the same family, but are less informative about the interaction of the underlying factors, and it was therefore decided to carry out a detailed clinical investigation, using as propositi the children attending a psychiatric clinic, for whom extensive observations regarding the psychiatric disorder, its development, and associations were available. Admittedly, this group of clinic children may not be representative of all children with neurotic and behavioural disorders but little is known of the characteristics of mentally ill children not attending clinics. The conclusions from this study can therefore only be applied to a wider population with the reservations implicit in a study of a clinic sample.

# CHAPTER I

# REVIEW OF THE LITERATURE: ILLNESS IN PARENTS AND THEIR CHILDREN

## I. MENTAL ILLNESS IN PARENTS AND PSYCHIATRIC DISORDER IN THEIR CHILDREN

PSYCHOPATHOLOGY and disorganization in patients' families have been considered from many viewpoints, including those of general medicine (Richardson, 1945), social anthropology (Folsom, 1934) and psychiatry (Post and Wardle, 1962). Major theoretical developments have centred on the role of the family in personality development (Parsons and Bales, 1955) and innumerable clinical reports have mentioned the deleterious effects on others of parental mental illness. Systematic studies of the association between psychiatric illness in parents and in their children, however, are few. They can be divided into those concerned with children of mentally ill adults, those dealing with the parents of children under psychiatric care, those concerned with family dysfunction as reflected in psychological tests, and, lastly, epidemiological studies. Although the interaction between parents and children is two-way, for present purposes only the effects of parental illness on the child will be considered, although effects on other members of the family will also be included if they relate to the interaction between parent and child.

### Children of Psychotic Adults

Studies of this kind have chiefly examined whether psychiatric illness in parents is associated with an increased likelihood of psychiatric disturbance in their children. Following on Thom's early survey of the offspring of epileptics (Thom and Walker, 1921), Canavan and Clark studied the 463 children of 136 married patients receiving the diagnosis of dementia praecox at the Boston Psychopathic Hospital between 1912 and 1921 (Canavan and Clark, 1923a). Eighty-two children had died; of the remainder only 12 were designated as 'nervous' and 36 had conduct disorders. The findings were compared with those in a study of 581 children of 145 married patients attending a medical out-patient department (Canavan and Clark, 1923b). Fewer children had conduct disorders (1·6 per cent.) than in the schizophrenic group (9·5 per cent.) a finding worthy of note, perhaps, in view of recent reports of a high incidence of schizophrenia in adults who were, in childhood, (at about the time Canavan and Clark's paper was written) treated for conduct disorders (O'Neal and Robins, 1958; O'Neal et al., 1960). Other conditions were roughly comparable, though the death rate was slightly higher and the rate of physical illness markedly lower among the children of dementia praecox patients. A further study on the same group of children of psychotic parents 13 years later showed rather more conduct disorders (27 out of 117 children), but over half the children were still quite normal (Canavan and Clark, 1936). The conclusion was that: '. . . the offspring of . . . dementia praecox patients show surprisingly few mental peculiarities'. However, the groups were not matched, a considerable number of schizophrenic families was not studied and the criteria for disorders in the children were not clearly stated. In addition, it is apparent that the children's ages differed in the two groups.

Canavan and Clark's study did not distinguish between offspring of adult age and those younger, although it is evident that the majority were still in childhood. Preston and Antin (1933) reported a study of all children under the age of 18 years whose parents were admitted to Baltimore public mental hospitals and diagnosed as psychotic. As a 'control' group, all children in the third and fifth grades of a somewhat better than average public school were chosen. The 'control' children showed rather more psychiatric abnormalities of all kinds: only 13·2 per cent. were normal, in comparison with 38·8 per cent. of the children of psychotics. These findings were compared with those of Ramage (1925) who produced figures almost identical with those of Canavan and Clark's earlier study. Preston and Antin concluded: '. . . that an actively psychotic parent who was fairly promptly committed to a state hospital was very much less detrimental than a fool parent who stayed at home'. The control group was, however, not comparable in several ways, and in particular the study of 'normals' was more thorough, so that it was to be expected that more abnormalities would be found. One might also remark on criteria (unstated) that enabled 86·8 per cent. of a 'normal' group to be regarded as 'abnormal'!

These writers appeared to assume that it is better for children that their psychotic parents be rapidly removed and incarcerated, but there is evidence that break-up of the family (Banister and Ravden, 1944 and 1945; Wardle, 1961), or separation of mother and child for prolonged periods (Bowlby et al., 1956) can have deleterious effects, although at times these have been overstated (Wootton, 1959). It would seem that the effect on the child is much related to what then happens to him (Wootton, 1959) and to the quality of care given by those who take over the parental role (Banister and Ravden, 1945). It is, therefore, important to determine the effect on the child of parental psychosis uncomplicated by other factors, such as removal to hospital. Sunier and Meijers (1951), from Amsterdam, reported an investigation of the effects of chronic psychosis, without mental deficiency, in a parent whose spouse was healthy and living with the family. Ten families, with 25 children, were studied; histories were obtained by social workers and all children were seen by the authors. Only one child had been referred to the Children's Department: at the age of 12 years, for 'maladjusted behaviour' towards his mother (the patient); on re-examination he was not markedly disturbed. Various neurotic difficulties were noted in three other children, but were thought to be strikingly slight and generally not to result from the psychosis. Children were more prone to be disturbed if personality difficulties were present in addition to the parental psychosis or if the other marriage partner was an unsatisfactory parent or was also psychiatrically ill. The problem of the psychotic parent was thought to differ from that of the neurotic or psychopathic parent, whose children more often had behaviour difficulties. Schoolchildren were often embarrassed by the oddities of their psychotic parents, much as are children having parents with a bodily or speech defect. The authors concluded that, if the family is otherwise normal and the sane partner can cope with difficulties that are necessarily greater than in a normal family, then: '. . . the occurrence and presence of a chronic psychosis of one of the parents . . . does not have serious consequences (for the child). . . .' They believed that it might often be preferable for a psychotic parent to remain at home, rather than be away from the children.

Ludy's study (1939) was unusual in finding an increased rate of 'maladjustment' among children of psychotic parents (12 out of 14 compared with 5 out of 14 control children). A well-matched control group was used but it was not stated how it was obtained (only a short abstract of the original thesis has been published), the numbers were too small for firm conclusions and it is not known whether the 14 children of 14 psychotic mothers were all the surviving children or whether there had been some selection.

Fifteen children born in a mental hospital to psychotic mothers were followed up and their later adjustment assessed by Gardner (1949). The babies who received less adequate mothering in hospital were, on the whole, less well adjusted than those who received good mothering, but only two children were badly maladjusted and none was severely neurotic or psychotic. Children placed in secure foster homes were better adjusted than those who went home with their families, where there was often much environmental stress and instability. The author concluded that: '. . . the hospital experience in itself was not the prime factor in the type of adjustment the children later made'.

Since 1959, Baker and his colleagues (1961) have had a unit at Banstead Hospital for puerperal schizophrenic mothers with their babies. Overt hostility to the child was only rarely observed and, with help and support from the nurses, the mothers were able to look after their babies throughout their hospital stay. Follow-up after discharge showed that many schizophrenics were good mothers, with much affection for their very young children, in spite of other abnormal relationships. The toddlers appeared well adjusted (more so, it was felt, than the very young of many neurotic mothers), but the schizophrenic mothers had more difficulty in coping with the older children. The recovery rate of mothers admitted with their babies was also better than for those admitted without them. Similar findings have been reported by other workers who have admitted psychotic mothers with their children (Grunebaum *et al.*, 1963 a and b; Weiss *et al.*, 1964).

Sussex (Sussex, 1963; Sussex *et al.*, 1963), who studied psychotic mothers treated at home, also found that many could meet the emotional needs of their children regardless of how much the illness had disrupted their life, or, if not, that other adults often substituted effectively for the mother when her 'mothering' capacities were impaired. For the four (out of 16) children who did show maladjustment during the mothers' illness, the mothers, although often no 'sicker', had lost the capacity to form adequate relationships with their children and there were no other adults to step into the breach.

Eight infants born to parents *both* of whom were schizophrenic were studied by Sobel (1961). Four, all born to mothers receiving in-patient care, were placed in foster homes; 18 months later none had shown any overt psychopathology. In contrast, all of three cared for by their schizophrenic (and also depressed) mothers showed sombre mood, irritability, lack of spontaneity, hypoactivity, and motor retardation. The mothers played little with their infants and appeared to lack positive feeling for them. It was hypothesized that the state of the children might represent depression 'learned' from the mother, or that the lack of maternal responses to the children might be important in constituting a relative absence of reinforcing behaviour.

In many ways, the most satisfactory study is that of Cowie (1961 a and b), although it was designed primarily to examine a rather limited genetical hypothesis. The incidence of neurotic disorders among the children of 132 psychotic in-patients was compared with that among a matched control group selected from patients attending hospitals because of physical illness or pregnancy. A full psychiatric history, with special attention to childhood development, was taken for each of the offspring, during interview with one or both parents. Bowlby's Teacher's Report Form and the Maudsley Personality Inventory were also used. Compared with the control group there was no overall increase in the incidence of neurotic disorder among the children of psychotic parents, but such neurosis as there was developed significantly more frequently during the two-year period after the onset of psychosis in the parent. On the other hand, neurotic disturbance was more frequent among the offspring of 20 obsessionals, the numbers being too small, however, for the finding to be more than suggestive.

The study was well planned; the groups were of adequate size and matched for age and sex, and the information obtained was extensive, but the 'children' included adults of up to middle age (although the age of the child did not appear to affect the likelihood of development of neurosis) and disorders of conduct or antisocial behaviour were not included. Truancy was grouped with neurotic symptoms—an association which might be questioned (Hersov, 1960 a and b). Of course, these criticisms apply to a use for which the study was not primarily intended and the important finding remains that neurotic symptoms do not occur more frequently among the children of psychotic parents than among the children of parents without mental illness, to confirm earlier investigations.

Studies agree in finding that psychosis in one parent is not a potent cause of disturbance in the children, but when the other parent is also psychotic or otherwise disturbed, and the child continues to be cared for by his parents, he may run a greater risk of child psychiatric disorder. However, few studies have distinguished acute and chronic disorders, and nearly all were carried out before the current trend towards earlier discharge and community care, i.e. most schizophrenics were in hospital and not in contact with their families. It cannot be assumed that the children would do as well if the psychotic parent remained at home and was treated as an out-patient.

From the point of view of the adult psychiatrist, the problem is fairly small as very few schizophrenics have children. Among the 500 urban psychotic patients of Preston and Antin's study (1933) only 27 had children under the age of 18 living with them up to the development of the psychosis. The proportion is unusually small by present-day standards, but probably the unmarried still preponderate among schizophrenics (Norris, 1956).

### Children of Neurotic and Psychopathic Parents

Although there have been many reports on this subject, systematic studies of the children of non-psychotic psychiatrically ill parents have been limited to two and unfortunately neither used a control group. Macdonald (1939) studied the social adjustment of the 58 children of 19 psychoneurotic women in-patients of the Massachusetts General Hospital. Two-thirds of the children were rated as having 'good' or 'fair' adjustment. There were more maladjusted boys than girls and the highest incidence of maladjustment was in the 6–13 years age group. Aberrant behaviour was always submissive in type; no cases of aggressive or delinquent disorders were found.

More recently Post (1962) in a study of the intra- and extra-familial contacts of non-schizophrenic, married, upper-working-class psychiatric patients attending the Bethlem and Maudsley hospitals, found high rates of psychiatric disorder in consanguineous and non-consanguineous contacts, both adults and children. Disorder was most common in the contacts of patients with a chronic or recurrent neurotic or affective disorder. Children were rated according to degree of maladjustment by an independent psychiatrist on the basis of questionnaires administered to one of the parents. Only 20 per cent. were deemed entirely free of problems; 34 per cent. were regarded as probably seriously disturbed. An important finding was that the offspring of patients termed 'psychotic' (on the basis of recent severe depression, feelings of guilt and self-reproach and/or delusional hypochondriasis) were far less often psychopathologically affected (14·3 per cent.) than the children of 'non-psychotic' patients, of whom two-fifths (42·8 per cent.) were regarded as definitely disturbed. Post concluded that interaction with a persistently ill parent, rather than heredity, seemed the more likely mechanism of transmission.

This problem of disentangling genetic and interactive effects in children is paralleled by the issue of psychiatric illnesses in husbands and wives, which are associated significantly more often than expected by chance (Kreitman, 1962; Nielson, 1964; Pond et al., 1963). Most previous writers emphasized assortative mating as an explanation (e.g. Gregory, 1959; Penrose, 1944) but Kreitman's finding that correlation on neuroticism between patients and their wives increased with duration of marriage strongly suggests that a spread of ill-health from one partner to the other is also important (Kreitman, 1964).

In 1955, in a special issue of the *Journal of Social Issues* on 'The Impact of Mental Illness on the Family', Clausen and Yarrow (the editors for that issue) stated that almost no systematically collected data existed to analyse what happens within a family when a member develops a mental illness. To remedy this, they reported an analysis of 33 families in which the husband was the patient (Clausen, 1959b; Clausen and Yarrow, 1955). The study was largely concerned with the effect upon the wife; the influence of parental illness was not specifically examined. However, of 18 families with children under the age of six years, in nearly all, the father's illness was initially concealed from the child, although in 14 families the children did eventually visit the father (Yarrow, Clausen and Robbins, 1955). The problems associated with recognition that the patient is mentally ill included the difficulty of assessing the significance of 'strange' behaviour, when the abnormalities fluctuated and when there was off-setting 'normal' behaviour (Yarrow, Schwartz, Murphy, and Deasy, 1955).

Sainsbury and Grad reported on the problems that 410 mentally ill people had been causing their families at the time of psychiatric referral (Grad and Sainsbury, 1963; Sainsbury and Grad, 1962). Relief of the family burden in the month after the patient came under psychiatric care was comparable in a community-care service and a hospital-centred service. Admission rates were high in both (57 per cent. and 74 per cent. respectively) but admission did not necessarily solve the family problems. The burden tended to be greater when there were children in the family and where the spouse had to look after the patient. Mills (1962) also studied the impact of mental illness on families. In neither study were children the chief focus of inquiry.

The effects on family life of leucotomy performed on one member have been studied by Lane (1956). Her group included eight married women with children still dependent and living at home. She commented: '...the children ... suffered not only from the mothers' casual behaviour and lack of feelings but also from parental conflict. In all the cases where there were young children they were, however, of an age when the relationship with the mother was no longer exclusive, and in several, separations had already occurred as the result of the mother's illness. As far as could be judged during the period the cases were under review, none of the children showed severe disturbance but several of them developed some behaviour problems in the home, though no great difficulties were noted at school. Where they were able to establish a secure and happy relationship with the father or other relative with whom they were in close contact the adjustment to the mother was made fairly quickly and easily in various ways of their own.'

Treudley (1946) discussed the impact on the family of psychiatric illness in one member, using 105 records of psychiatric patients, 48 from a large mental hospital and the rest from two family welfare societies. Important factors were the effects on family finances, relationships with neighbours, and care of children. A sick parent might insist on a child sleeping with him or her for protection against morbid fears, or children might be kept at home from school to care for the sick parent. This applied especially to adolescent daughters upon whom parental mental illness was thought to bear most heavily. Children might also feel the effect of the social stigma of mental illness; it was thought that boys commonly reacted by running away, whereas girls tended to cut themselves off from the community. Unfortunately the records were not regarded as suitable for statistical analysis and no figures were given. More recently, Radinsky (1961) discussed the issue in terms of the problems of a foster care agency. She concluded that there was '. . . a considerable risk in reintroducing into the child's life a parent who has been seriously mentally ill'.

The Cassel Hospital was one of the first to consider, as part of the treatment of maternal psychiatric illness, the effect of the illness on the children. In 1955, young children were for the first time admitted with their psychiatrically ill (but not psychotic) mothers (Main, 1958). Gluck and Wrenn (1959) reported on a study of some of these women admitted with their pre-school children for psychoanalytically oriented group psychotherapy. The children seemed to re-enact in their play the things their mother did to them. Some of the mothers had presented their children's problems as their own leading symptoms. Two illustrative cases were discussed.

Pauline Morris (1958) described relationships in families admitted to the Social Rehabilitation Unit at Belmont Hospital (now the Henderson Hospital). Marital discord and sexual maladjustment were found in all married patients in the sample, either as a presenting symptom or as an effect of the illness: 'the psychiatric illness of one member inevitably presents a distinct social problem, in that the balance of inter-personal relationships is disturbed'. The effect on the children was not specifically studied. Gruenberg and Bellin (1957) discussed the disruptive consequences for the family of mental disorder in one member. They stressed the sharp contrast between reaction to 'mental illness' as an abstract and to Mr. X as a mentally ill person with whom one is in close contact. The question was raised whether the consequences for the family might markedly differ according to which parent

B

is ill. Cleveland and Longaker (1957) considered neurotic patterns in the family, and described one family to illustrate the viewing of neurosis in its cultural and familial context. Ehrenwald (1958) has discussed neurotic interaction in the family in what he described as patterns of pseudo-heredity, giving as an example a family with a high incidence of obsessive-compulsive neurotics in three generations. This, he thought, might be explained by the effects of contagion in the transmission of neurotic traits. The association of neurotic disorders in parents and children has also been stressed by Hopkins (1959) and Apley (1963).

Seven mothers who exhibited homicidal wishes towards their children were reported on by Stern (1948). Three had attended because of disorder in their children, who had been brought to a child guidance clinic. The hostility towards the child was thought to represent revenge against the father. Women with compulsive murderous ideas towards their children have also been studied by Anthony (Anthony, 1959; Foulkes and Anthony, 1957), who for four years conducted analytic group psychotherapy with 12 such women. The setting in which the murderous ideas developed was not uniform; the diagnoses included obsessional neurosis, depression, anxiety hysteria and 'explosive' psychopathy. Of the children, half were overtly disturbed and two severely so. Children of inhibited parents were outwardly aggressive whereas children of more violent women were passive and fearful.

Doniger (1962), in a study of the families of 83 women who were mental hospital in-patients, noted how children were sometimes involved in their mother's delusions and commented on the problem of treating children who were living with a psychotic mother. Close liaison between hospital and local authority services is required. Irvine (1961) also emphasized the importance of considering the family of the psychiatric patient. Winnicott (1961) considered the effects of illness in terms of the child's stage of development. He believes that only the mother is important in early infancy, whereas both parents are important for older children. It is sometimes necessary to remove children from psychotic or severely neurotic parents if the adverse effect on the children is marked.

Before any of the foregoing studies, though not commented on in any, Janet (1925) reported careful observations on a large number of cases, and subsequent clinical descriptions have added little to what he said then. In 18 cases there was an association between psychiatric disorder in fathers and psychiatric illness in their sons and daughters, 6 cases being detailed. In several families many members were affected, and there were three cases of illness in step-parents and their children. Janet noted several instances in which children brought up away from the family escaped the affliction, and concluded that the association was mainly due not to a genetic link but rather to 'social fatigue' induced by living with neurotics. The direct effect of neurotic behaviour upon other members of the family was described. Janet thought that imitation was rarely important; it was more the effect of illness on the social life of others in the family, in whom the neurosis maintained psychological tension.

*Parents of Children with Psychiatric Disorder*

The studies so far discussed have all started from the sick parent. Another approach is by way of the child who has a psychiatric disorder and also a mentally-ill relative. There have been many studies of neurotic parental attitudes and influences, but few of mental illness in the parents, although this receives passing mention in many papers.

Huschka (1941) based a study on the clinical records of problem children seen by her over a period of three years at the New York Hospital; most had been referred through the Paediatric Department and most were paying patients. Six hundred and five children were seen and 488 were studied. Psychopathological manifestations, including neurotic symptoms, guilt, depression, suicidal impulses or paranoid trends were found in 203 (41·6 per cent.) of the mothers, 30 of whom had attended the psychiatric out-patient department, all but two being diagnosed as psychoneurotic. The mother's illness was thought important in that, '. . . one characteristic of these cases is that whatever the mother's symptom picture, it covers every stage of the child's emotional development and influences him accordingly'. The children's symptoms were not tabulated but, in the cases described, appeared to be mainly neurotic. The author believed that '. . . the patterns . . . are distinctly individual and do not lend themselves readily to classification into subgroups with, common characteristics, . . . classification . . . runs the risk of superficial evaluation, thereby clouding the issue and standing in the way of a more penetrating understanding of the symptomatic behaviour calling for treatment'.

Although every psychiatric disorder is unique, each has characteristics in common with others, and by which it can be classified. This may be difficult or arbitrary, but to regard every patient and every disorder as *entirely* individual is a retrograde step (Kanner, 1959).

Fabian and Donohue (1956) found depression especially common in the mothers of children attending a guidance clinic. They stressed the importance of *maternal* depression, but believed that the effect might be the same when a mother-surrogate took over the mothering role; this might be a relative, maid, foster-parent or even the father. Depression was described as having a wide variety of effects including murderous hostility to the child, or reaction formation leading to a caricature of over-cautious behaviour. Abnormalities in the children took many forms; autistic states, sticky identification reminiscent of 'folie à deux', infantilism, psychosomatic ailments, neuroses, and behaviour disorders.

Similarly, Campbell (1952), noted in a series of 18 children with manic-depressive or depressive reactions, that 14 had a positive family history of manic-depressive disease. Unfortunately, no criteria were given for the limits of 'family' but it is clear that in at least 5 cases a parent had been the sick relative. Although the illnesses were regarded as hereditary, the author stated: '. . . A cyclothymic child cannot adjust well in a home where there is a manic-depressive parent'. Two illustrative cases were given.

A different approach was presented by Horn (1954) in a series of 20 child-patients with a psychotic relative (usually the father), and in which the mother identified the child with the sick relative. The mothers generally regarded the child's disorder as hereditary although often blaming the child for his symptoms. Half the mothers had fears about their own mental stability and all but one showed marked neurotic tendencies, the identification thus often being partly a projection of the mother's concern about herself. Sixteen mothers rejected their children and in all 16 this attitude antedated the identification of the child with the psychotic relative, this identification appearing as a rationalization of their own hostility.

Hilda Lewis (1954), in her comprehensive study of *Deprived Children*, demonstrated in children admitted to a reception centre a significant correlation between 'maternal insanity or psychopathy' and the severity of the child's disturbance at admission. As this factor was but one of many studied, the criteria for diagnosis of illness were not made explicit, but the children's disorders were classified on the basis of Hewitt and Jenkins' factor analytic study (1946). Using their syndrome groupings, Hilda Lewis found that neurotic reactions were particularly common in the children of neurotic and psychopathic mothers. The associations were shown to be statistically significant.

Neurosis and affective disorders were found by Hersov (1958) to be commoner in the parents of children with neurotic school refusal than in the parents of truants, or in the parents of a random sample of children attending the same clinic but falling into neither group. These differences remained significant when the criteria were narrowed to include only parents under psychiatric care. Bowlby in his study of *Forty-four Juvenile Thieves* (1946) found that only 4 had a psychotic parent, compared with nine in a similar-sized control group of unselected children attending the London Child Guidance Clinic. A further 10 had a neurotic or psychopathic parent as against 6 in the control group. Litauer (1957) found parental psychiatric illness (usually maternal neurosis) in 67 (26·5 per cent.) of a group of juvenile delinquents attending the Portman Clinic. There were comparatively more younger children than adolescents with neurotic parents. Morris, Escoll, and Wexler (1956) comparing 90 children who had aggressive behaviour disorders with 60 who had post-encephalitic behaviour disorders, found an excess of all forms of mental illness in the former.

Nathan Ackerman has written widely on the importance of an integrative approach to the family (see, for example, Ackerman, 1956a and b, 1958; Ackerman and Behrens, 1956), has stressed the influence on others in the family of illness in one member, and has suggested that a 'psychosocial diagnosis of the family' should be made. 'Psychiatric illness as a single or isolated instance in family life hardly occurs. Almost always other members of the family are also ill. The sick behaviours of these family members are often closely woven and mutually reinforcing' (Ackerman, 1958). His work so far has not included a systematic study of interaction between psychiatrically ill members of a family.

Otto Pollak (Pollak and collaborators, 1952) emphasized that emotional disturbances of children are often created by emotional disturbances in those about them, and that the social environment of one person is a combination of the intrapsychic problems of others. In contrast to most writers, Pollak stressed the influence of the father as much as that of the mother. Szasz (1959) considered that the child, even more than the adult, is prone to think that if mother is upset, he must have caused it, and that this is one of the reasons for a child to develop disturbance reactive to parental mental illness. Parallels between the conflicts and anxieties of children and those of their parents have been claimed by Rank, Putnam, and Rochlin (1947) but they presented little evidence in support. Elles (1961) also, in an account of a depressive disorder involving both parents and two children, has commented on the link between the fantasies of mothers and their children.

Koch (1939) observed that neurotic children often had neurotic parents but, because the neuroses were frequently dissimilar, considered that the link was not primarily genetic, although the 'weak constitution' was inherited. Neurotic fathers, as well as mothers, were affected by their own complexes in bringing up their children. Child neurosis, she believed, was related to 'conflicts', but the neuroses were more extensive and severe if the parents were also neurotic.

None of the studies based on child-patients has systematically examined associations between illnesses in parents and their children, but many have provided clinical descriptions. An excess of parental mental disorders of all sorts has sometimes been found (Morris et al., 1956), sometimes 'maternal insanity or psychopathy' (Lewis, 1954), but more usually parental neurosis (Hersov, 1960; Huschka, 1941; Litauer, 1957) or depression (Fabian and Donohue, 1956), rather than psychosis, has been emphasized.

*Psychological Testing of Families*

Psychological tests, which may reflect psychopathology, offer an indirect approach to the association of illness in members of the same family. Abrahamson (1960) gave the *Cornell Medical Index* to mothers and daughters in a part of Durban, selecting all families in which the daughter was an unmarried Hindu girl of 16 or 17 years, living at home with her mother. There were positive correlations between the scores of mothers and their daughters, mostly on questions regarding emotional health and particularly on the anxiety section where the correlation was $0.58$ ($p < 0.001$). M.M.P.I. (Minnesota Multiphasic Personality Inventory) profiles of parents of children referred to a psychiatric clinic were studied by Hanvik and Byrum (1959). None of the correlations between parental M.M.P.I. profile scores and the classification of children's behaviours was statistically significant, but mothers with high D scale scores tended to have children with a 'school-phobia syndrome'. The Pd-Ma differential was often very high, reputedly reflecting severe marriage problems. Marks (1961) found that parents of children attending a child guidance clinic differed from the general population on most personality variables measured by the M.M.P.I. In a similar investigation by Lauterbach et al. (1961) such parents had their higher scores on the Hs, Hy and Pd scales (the so-called 'neurotic triad'). In general, scores were midway between those for normals and those for neurotics.

Projective tests have also been given to patients and their relatives, and similarities in responses and scores claimed (Fisher and Mendell, 1956; Morris and Nicholas, 1950; Rosenzweig and Isham, 1947). The last authors claimed that a family specific 'neurotic pattern' pervaded the projective expressions of different members of one family, and, to explain why with such similarity in neurotic patterns only one member overtly broke down, suggested that the family 'chooses' a special respresentative to seek outside help, in an attempt to heal the issues which disturb the whole family. Their suggestion appears to have little factual basis.

*Epidemiological Studies*

Jean Downes carried out a longitudinal morbidity study of families living in a defined area of Baltimore. Each family was visited monthly and reports of illness were checked with the attending physician (Downes, 1942, 1945, 1950, 1951, and 1952). Families with an index case of major chronic illness differed from the general population in having an excess rate of illness (Downes, 1942). In 90 of these families the chronic illness was psychoneurosis or 'nervousness'. As compared with the 828 other families, including a member with a chronic but non-psychiatric condition, the 90 families with a psychiatric patient contained a highly significant excess of chronic illness in members other than the index case (Downes, 1952; Downes and Simon, 1953 and 1954). The differences could not be explained in terms of social conditions as the groups did not differ in respect of such factors as mobility, crowding, income, home ownership, education level of adults, and marital status.

This approach was carried further with regard to neurosis by Buck and Laughton (1959). They used the continuous medical records over a five-year period of members of 115 families, part of a five per cent. random sample of subscribers to a comprehensive pre-paid medical care plan in Windsor, Canada. Their report concerned the 65 families with children, where there were complete records for both husband and wife. The children of neurotic mothers (but not of neurotic fathers) had a significant excess of behavioural, psychosomatic and traumatic disorders. The differences were large—for example, the mean number of behavioural and psychosomatic illness episodes per child was 1·3 when the mother was neurotic, compared with a mean of 0·4 when neither parent was neurotic.

The authors examined two possible artifacts which might have accounted for the differences. The first, that the physician who was aware of psychiatric illness in the parents might have been more apt to diagnose behavioural and psychosomatic disorders in the children, was thought unlikely to have been operative, as differences were even more marked when parents and children had seen different physicians. The second, that the presence of a psycho-neurotic mother might have increased the frequency with which the child was taken to the doctor for all classes of illness, was also examined. Children's minor illnesses, where the seeking of medical attention depended largely on the mothers' views, were used to measure maternal use of services. After the results had been corrected for this the children of neurotic mothers still showed an excess of behavioural and psychosomatic disorders, suggesting that the excess was a true one.

This study offers the most satisfactory demonstration of an excess of psychiatric disorder in the children of neurotic parents, and has recently been supported by a British study of general practice (Kellner, 1963). Starting from the observation that illnesses in a family often came in pairs or clusters, Kellner showed a particular interaction between neurotic disorders in fathers and mothers, and between mothers and children, but, like Buck and Laughton, little between fathers and their children. On the other hand, in an epidemiological study of family illness in Croydon, Hare and Shaw (1965) found that physical and mental ill-health in either mothers or fathers were associated with an increased rate of behaviour disorder in the children.

Studies have been described which suggest that this excess of child psychiatric disorder is not found in the offspring of psychotic parents. Although various suggestions have been made regarding ways in which a sick parent may have a deleterious influence on the child, the relationships between forms of parental illness and forms of childhood disorder have been little explored.

## II. PHYSICAL ILLNESS IN PARENTS AND PSYCHIATRIC DISORDER IN THEIR CHILDREN

Parental physical illness has often been noted in accounts of either single child patients or groups of maladjusted or delinquent children, but there have been scarcely any investigations into relationships, causal or otherwise, between such illness and psychiatric disorder in the offspring.

The work of Jean Downes, from the Eastern Health District of Baltimore, has already been mentioned in connection with parental psychiatric illness. Families tended to have similar illness rates over a three-year period and the illness of one child often reflected the state of health of his sibs (Downes, 1945). Members of families which contained an index case of chronic illness had an excess rate of illness in comparison with the remaining population, which could not be explained in terms of social differences (Downes, 1942). The excess was most marked when the chronic illness was neurotic (Downes and Simon, 1953), but was also present with other diagnoses. The association with child psychiatric disorder was not specifically studied, but Ciocco et al. (1954) found, in a study of 2,370 Pittsburgh families, that family ill-health was associated with an increased contact with social agencies. Reasons for such contacts included juvenile delinquency, children's behaviour problems, disorders of parent-offspring relationships and marital disorders.

The Gluecks, in their now classical study of 500 institutionalized delinquent boys, found that 198 (39·6 per cent.) of the fathers had a 'serious physical ailment', compared with just over a quarter (28·6 per cent.) of the fathers of non-delinquent boys (S. and E. Glueck, 1950). There was a similar excess of physically ill mothers, half (48·6 per cent.) compared with a third (33·0 per cent.) of the control group. Both differences were significant at the 1 per cent. level. The delinquent and non-delinquent groups were both living in an under-privileged area of Boston and were well matched for age, I.Q., and ethnic origin, but as the delinquents had all been committed to correctional schools, it is uncertain how far differences were due to factors leading to commitment of the child by the authorities, rather than factors leading to the child becoming delinquent—an important distinction. In addition, as physical illness occurs at some time in all people, it is unfortunate that the term 'serious physical ailment' was not defined.

Terms were also not defined in other studies, including one of delinquents attending a psychiatric clinic (Litauer, 1957), where parental physical illness was found to be more frequent among what were termed 'clinical offenders'. Holman (1953) in her study of children attending a child guidance clinic also noted a high incidence of parental illness, and Bennett (1960) found high rates of chronic parental illness in respect of both neurotic and delinquent children. Parental physical deformity was also equally frequent in the two groups. Craig (1956), in a study of 200 children with behaviour disorders, noted that parental physical illness sometimes precipitated or contributed to the child's maladjustment. Illness impaired the energy of the parents and made them irritable and irascible with the children.

The only direct study of children of chronically ill parents is that of Arnaud (1959), who investigated a sample of 60 children of patients attending a multiple sclerosis clinic. The children were aged 7 to 16 years, were all living with both parents, and had been exposed to the parental illness for a mean period of 7·2 years. Rorschach responses were compared with those of 221 children of comparable age, intelligence, and social background. The method of obtaining the control population was not described. Some statistically significant differences were found. For example, the children of parents with multiple sclerosis showed more responses taken to indicate bodily concern, dysphoria, hostility, dependency longings, constraint in inter-personal relations, and 'false maturity'. In the children under 13 years there were also higher scores on 'diffuse anxiety'. The results are of interest, but it is a pity that other methods of comparison were not employed as well, for the deficiencies of the Rorschach test (Payne, 1955) (particularly low reliability and lack of demonstrable validity) leave responses open to many interpretations, none of which can be accepted without question.

The effect upon the children of a parent's severe disablement has been mentioned on various occasions but in only one report has the matter received particular study. Canadian workers investigated eight families in which the father had received a sudden severe disablement from which there had been not more than 70 per cent. recovery (De la Mata et al., 1960). In none of the families was the home 'broken', nor was there any overt psychopathology. The stress on the dynamic equilibrium of the family was severe, but tended to be less if the father eventually returned to work. Previously good integration of the family and flexibility in role functioning aided readjustment. Adolescent children thought more in terms of disruption of the family unit. On the other hand, the younger ones, though they missed their father as a functioning person, tended to react more to the unrest and prevalent mood of the home.

Ekdahl's recent study of children whose parents had been admitted to hospital (Ekdahl et al., 1962) is particularly valuable. It covered 56 families with a parent admitted to hospital for mental illness and 28 where the parent was admitted because of tuberculosis. Disruption in living arrangements because of the admission was common to both groups. It was much greater when the mother was in hospital; children in 22 of the 54 families of mothers admitted to hospital were moved from their own homes to live in a variety of home situations, but in only one of the 30 families where the fathers were admitted to hospital did the children go to stay with relatives. Problems concerning the care of the children sometimes led to bitter family arguments which added to the children's distress. Problems of child-care were much greater if the parent admitted was the sole parent, and in these cases help from community resources was often delayed, inadequate, or not provided. The families of tuberculosis patients were better off on the whole because: (1) there was usually more time before admission in which to make suitable arrangements; (2) people's attitudes towards tuberculosis were more favourable and help more forthcoming; (3) the approximate length of stay in hospital was more often known for tuberculosis patients and so made planning easier; and (4) although the initial period of hospital care was longer, tuberculosis patients had fewer re-admissions. In both groups of families about half said their children were definitely 'upset' by what had happened. However, unlike the tuberculosis families, children of mentally ill parents were sometimes involved in the symptomatology of the parents' illness. For example, in one family the father destroyed all the children's toys; in another the children did not want to stay in the same house as their father; in two families the children were abused and threatened with a knife; in several families the parent frightened and confused the children by telling strange stories, in two families the daughters were sexually attacked; in several the mother physically neglected the child.

Problems for the children tend to be similar when parents are admitted to hospital regardless of the reason. Evidence suggests that chronic illness, physical or mental, may be associated with the development of psychiatric disorder in the children. Perhaps the main way in which mental and physical parental illnesses differ in their impact on the child is that the symptoms of mental illness may be more directly deleterious. However, the data are meagre and the need for a detailed clinical study of all kinds of illness in the parents of children attending a psychiatric clinic led to the present investigation.

# CHAPTER II

# OUTLINE OF STUDY

ALL children who attended The Maudsley Hospital Children's Department[1] for the first time in the years 1955 and 1959 were studied. The first year was chosen because nearly all patients registered in 1955 would have completed treatment by the time of this study and the second because it was the most recent year when the study was started. There were 12 sets of notes missing for 1955, 7 in the same year had to be excluded because data were inadequate, and 6 in 1959 for the same reason. This left 922 patients, 461 in each year, who form the basis of this study.

As there was a uniform system of history-taking, examination, and recording of information for children attending the Department the records were fairly uniform in style and quality. They were abstracted by the author according to defined categories.[2] Whenever the records stated that either parent had been seen by a psychiatrist at any time, or had had a psychiatric illness, the hospital or clinic where they had attended was contacted and the records abstracted in the same way. In a few cases a summary only was obtainable.

## Subdivision of Groups of Children

The group of 922 children was subdivided according to the diagnosis of the child. To be included in the main study the child had to have a neurotic or conduct disorder of some kind. In practice most children had been diagnosed as having 'primary childhood behaviour disorder' (No. 324 of the International Classification of Diseases—I.C.D.). Diagnoses also included personality disorder (I.C.D. Numbers 320, 321) and psychoneurotic disorders (I.C.D. Numbers 310–318). A few diagnoses were made under other headings. Such a broad definition seemed preferable to pre-judging the issue by excluding certain groups such as delinquents. For comparisons within it the group was further subdivided according to defined diagnostic categories.

Cases in which neurotic or behavioural disorders were complicated by epilepsy but not directly caused by it (that is, the disorder was not a manifestation of an epileptic attack) were included. This was on the basis of Grunberg and Pond's finding (1957) that the background (genetic and environmental) of epileptic children with conduct disorders resembled that

---

[1] 'The Maudsley Hospital' is used throughout to refer to The Joint Maudsley and Bethlem Royal Hospitals. Similarly, the term 'Children's Department' is used to include the wards for children and for adolescents as well as the Out-patients Department.

[2] Definitions are included in the APPENDIX.

of non-epileptic children with conduct disorders and was strikingly different from that of epileptic children who exhibited no conduct disorder. In all, the group of neurotic and behaviour disorders comprised 739 children and will be termed the '*disturbed*' group.

Thirty-six psychotic or schizophrenic children were excluded. Children diagnosed as having 'no psychiatric abnormality', mental deficiency without other behaviour disturbance, epilepsy without a non-epileptic behaviour disorder, or an organic illness (usually of the central nervous system) were combined in a group of 147, the '*non-disturbed*' group. They had been referred to The Maudsley Hospital but had been judged either to be without psychiatric abnormality or to have some uncomplicated 'organic' condition. The main comparisons are between the '*disturbed*' group and control groups of Dental and Paediatric children [see below]. However, as a check, internal comparisons between the '*disturbed*' and '*non-disturbed*' groups were also made.

## Comparison Groups of Children

The first aim was to test the hypothesis that there would be significantly high rates of parental illness of all kinds among children with psychiatric disorder. To have a group of children without psychiatric disorder for comparison, and as the ideal of a random sample of the population was not practicable, data were obtained on children attending the Dental and Paediatric Departments of King's College Hospital, and an out-patient clinic at the Belgrave Hospital for Children.

As most children attend the dentist, a group of children attending a dental clinic was thought likely to give as fair a sample of the general population as could be obtained. There was no reason to suppose that the group would be biased in terms of psychiatric illness, although, as in most conditions, psychiatric factors have sometimes been thought to play a part in dental disorders (Ewen, 1952). As both King's College Hospital and The Maudsley Hospital are teaching hospitals situated in the same road, it seemed probable that the groups from which the patients were drawn would not be too dissimilar (and therefore not appreciably distorted by the matching procedure), although, as the selection factors which led to referral were unknown in both, they could not be assumed to be the same.

Three clinics (the Orthodontic, Conservation and Casual Attendance Clinics) were attended by the author over a period of five months in 1960 and, while each child received treatment, the accompanying parent was interviewed for about 10 to 15 minutes. Children in the care of a local or other authority were excluded. Detailed information was obtained on the composition of the home; occupation of the head of the household; psychiatric illness in the child, sibs, or parents; and similarly any physical illness in which incapacity lasted one month or longer.

In all, the parents of 243 children were seen. This Dental group contained fewer adolescents than the Maudsley group so, for the comparison, children aged 14 years or more, or in care, or with foster-parents were excluded from both groups. The groups were matched for age and social class (according to the *Registrar General's Classification of Occupations*) [TABLES 2.1 and 2.2 in APPENDIX], and the 259 Maudsley '*disturbed*' children who first attended in 1959 were compared with the 145 Dental children (other original group of 243 having been reduced by the matching).

Data were also obtained for children attending the out-patient clinics of the Paediatric Department of King's College Hospital and the associated clinic at the Belgrave Hospital for Children. This group was studied because, in the first place, children attending a Paediatric clinic were likely to include some with organic and some with psychiatric disorders. If so, this would provide an opportunity to check within the Paediatric group findings obtained by comparing the Maudsley and control groups. Secondly, as this group had been referred to hospital by general practitioners, light might be thrown on possible referral biases.

Parents were interviewed in the same way as for the Dental group. The clinic at King's College Hospital was attended by the author from September 1959 to July 1960 and that at the Belgrave Hospital from September 1959 to April 1960, and the parents of 275 children were seen. Unfortunately, unlike the Dental group, the age distribution at the Paediatric clinics differed very considerably from the Maudsley population. There was a marked preponderance of children aged 5 years or less, and very few children over 11 years. To match for age and social class an upper age limit of 11 years was set and the final matched group numbered 80. [TABLES 2.3 and 2.4 giving matching are in the APPENDIX.]

The frequency of parental psychiatric illness, acute, recurrent, and chronic physical illness,[1] and parental deaths was then compared between the matched Dental and Maudsley groups and the matched Paediatric and Maudsley groups. As the parental deaths in the control groups were few, the chief comparison was with the expected number of deaths as calculated from figures given by the Registrar General. The method is described in the APPENDIX.

*Subdivision according to Parental Illness*

The next question was whether children with parents who were ill differed in any way from other children attending the same clinic.

The '*disturbed*' group was first broken down into three parts: (1) 137 children of whom one or more parents had or had had a psychiatric illness (the '*psychiatric*' group); (2) children whose parents had a psychiatric illness for the first time while the child attended The Maudsley Hospital (this group numbered only 10 and, although examined, is omitted from the tables for the sake of simplification), and (3) 592 children neither of whose parents had a

---
[1] For definitions of illness see APPENDIX.

psychiatric illness (the 'other' group). Psychiatric illness was defined as: 'Any illness for which the person consulted a psychiatrist and which had been diagnosed as a psychiatric disorder, or any completed suicide, or any attempted suicide for which the person had consulted a doctor.' The 'psychiatric' and 'other' groups were then compared on relevant variables.

The difficulties of defining mental illness for any survey have been well reviewed by Clausen (1959a). If study is confined to patients seen at hospital, many minor neurotic conditions prevalent in general practice (Shepherd et al., 1959) are omitted. On the other hand, to include them makes diagnosis less reliable (Clausen, 1959a) and opens the way for biases in determining what constitutes 'illness'. These difficulties are greatly increased in any retrospective study. Attention was therefore confined to parents seen by psychiatrists, for whom greater details of the illness would be available. Suicidal acts were included as these were readily defined and, as disruptive events, might have considerable impact on the child. Of the 165 cases of parental psychiatric illness, 12 were suicidal acts and of 16 cases in the control group, 1 came under this category.

The 'disturbed' group was also broken down according to parental physical illness: (1) 95 children of whom one or more parents had during the child's lifetime a chronic physical illness[1] (the 'chronic' group); (2) 95 children of whom one or more parents had during the child's lifetime a recurrent physical illness (the 'recurrent' group); (3) 549 children of whom neither parent had had a chronic or recurrent physical illness (the 'other' group). The 'chronic', 'recurrent' and 'other' groups were compared in the same way as the 'psychiatric' and 'other' groups. Finally, 85 'bereaved' children (those who had lost one or both parents through death, irrespective of cause of death) were compared with non-bereaved children in the sample.

Reports of illness experienced some years previously are likely to be inaccurate about the nature of the illness, its duration and when it occurred, so that any but crude comparison would not be justifiable, therefore study was chiefly confined to illnesses lasting continuously or intermittently for at least a year (the 'chronic' and 'recurrent' groups respectively). Illnesses lasting less than one month were disregarded, but those lasting between 1 and 12 months were included, even though information on these was probably less satisfactory. For only a few cases could further reports be obtained from hospitals or other sources on the nature of the illnesses, and breakdown into diagnostic groups had to be confined to the system involved (cardio-respiratory, gastrointestinal, etc.).

Data on parental illness for the Maudsley children were obtained solely from the case notes. However, questions regarding parental health and illnesses are asked routinely, according to a schedule issued to doctors working in the Department. All or nearly all illnesses of more than a year's duration are likely to have been recorded. Less confidence can be placed on the record-

---

[1] Definitions of acute, recurrent and chronic physical illness are given in the APPENDIX.

ing of briefer illnesses although these, too, were generally mentioned if they had occurred. Information on parental illness in the Dental and Paediatric groups was in all cases obtained from the author's interviews with the parent or parents, in which specific questions were asked about illnesses as defined.

The selection of groups is summarized diagrammatically in FIGURE 2.1.

922 Children
attended The Maudsley Hospital
for any reason in 1955 or 1959,
of these:

   (i)  36  were Psychotic (excluded)
  (ii)  147[1] were 'Non-Disturbed'
 (iii)  739[2] were 'Disturbed'

| *of 739 'Disturbed' Children grouped according to Mental Illness in their Parents:* | *of 739 'Disturbed' Children* | *of 739 'Disturbed' Children grouped according to Physical Illness in their Parents:* |
|---|---|---|
| (i) [3]137 had one or more parents with Mental Illness. The *'Psychiatric'* Group. | 85 were Bereaved | (i) 95 had one or more parents with Chronic Physical Illness. The *'Chronic'* Group. |
| (ii) 592 had neither parent with Mental Illness. The *'Other'* Group. | | (ii) 95 had one or more parents with Recurrent Physical Illness. The *'Recurrent'* Group. |
| (iii) 10 had parents treated for Mental Illness *after* the child attended The Maudsley Hospital (excluded). | | (iii) 549 had neither parent with Chronic or Recurrent Physical Illness. The *'Other'* Group. |

[1] 100 when matched against the *'Disturbed'* Children.

[2] 532 when matched against the *'Non-Disturbed'* Children.
159 when matched against the Paediatric ('Control') Group ⎫ Children attending
259 when matched against the Dental ('Control') Group ⎭ in 1959 only.

[3] Of the parents of the 137 children in the Psychiatric Group, 48 first attended The Maudsley Hospital as out-patients. These form the Parental Group 1 [See FIGURE 2.2].

FIG. 2.1. DIAGRAM SHOWING SELECTION OF GROUPS OF CHILDREN

## Comparison Group of Parents

To determine what types or aspects of parental psychiatric illness were associated with psychiatric disorder in the children, a random group of psychiatrically ill parents whose children were psychiatrically healthy was ideal, but one could not be obtained. As the most suitable approach to the question, parents of 'disturbed' children who had themselves attended The

Maudsley Hospital were compared with the appropriate control group, a random sample of Maudsley patients who were also parents.

The scatter of years during which the parents (of Maudsley children) had attended The Maudsley Hospital was rather wide (1943 to 1959) but the majority had attended between 1953 and 1956, with 1954 as the peak year. As the diagnostic and other characteristics remain fairly stable from one period to another (*Triennial Statistical Report 1955–7*), patients who first attended in 1954 were selected for comparison. Taking at random a starting point during the year, the notes of a consecutive series of patients who first attended as out-patients were examined. All patients in whom no psychiatric disorder was found were excluded, as were 10 patients whose records could not be traced.

As a hospital with post-graduate teaching and research responsibilities, the Maudsley exercises considerable selection of patients for in-patient care or investigation. No selection is exercised regarding out-patients—any patient referred is seen, although, doubtless, there is some selection by referral agencies. For this reason, it was decided to exclude cases admitted directly without out-patient attendance and also cases seen first on a domiciliary consultation. A group of 527 patients first seen as out-patients was obtained (similar selection was made in the parent group). To make the groups comparable, selection was confined to patients (married or single) who had children of 17 years of age or younger, reducing the number to 200. From the records of these 200 patients data on the illness, family composition, occupation of head of the household, and psychiatric state of the spouse and children were abstracted.

From the group of 200 patients all those whose records mentioned psychiatric disorder in the children were put aside. Psychiatric disorder was taken to apply to any children who had received psychiatric treatment at any time, who had court convictions, or who were manifestly so severely disturbed that treatment was clearly required. Neurotic traits, 'difficult' behaviour, or anxiety were not in themselves sufficient for the child to be regarded as psychiatrically ill. In this way 31 cases were excluded (17 with children who had received psychiatric treatment, 2 with children who had had court convictions, and 12 others). Finally, three groups were obtained for comparisons: *Group 1*, 48 parents of '*disturbed*' children (all parents had attended The Maudsley Hospital as out-patients in the first instance), *Group 2*, 169 Maudsley patients all of whose children were less than 18 years of age and, as far as was known, psychiatrically well, *Group 3*, the 31 Maudsley patients whose children had psychiatric disorder. The first two groups were compared to determine what features of parental psychiatric illness were related to the development of psychiatric disorder in the children. To check the findings *Group 3* (the Maudsley patients with children with psychiatric disorder) was compared with *Group 1* (the mentally-ill parents of '*disturbed*' children). The selection of groups is summarized in FIGURE 2.2.

527 Consecutive Adult Patients
first seen as out-patients,
of these:

(i) 327 were without children OR
had no children younger than
17 years (excluded).

(ii) 200 had children of 17 years
or younger.

| *of the Parents of 137 children in the Psychiatric Group:* | *of 200 Patients with children of 17 years or younger:* | *of 200 Patients with children of 17 years or younger:* |
|---|---|---|
| 48 first attended the Maudsley Hospital as out-patients. | 169 had children who were well as far as was known. | 31 had children who were known to have had psychiatric disorder. |
| *Group 1* | *Group 2* | *Group 3* |

* See FIGURE 2.1.

FIG. 2.2. DIAGRAM SHOWING SELECTION OF GROUPS OF PARENTS

*Comparisons between Illnesses in Parents and Disorder in the Children*

Finally the parental illnesses were compared with the disorders in the children to determine whether particular types of parental illness were differentially associated with particular types of disorder in the child.

C

# CHAPTER III

# THE INCIDENCE OF PARENTAL ILLNESS

## I. PARENTAL PSYCHIATRIC ILLNESS IN MAUDSLEY, DENTAL, AND PAEDIATRIC GROUPS

AMONG the 461 patients who attended The Maudsley Hospital Children's Department in 1955, 66 (14·2 per cent.) had a parent or parents who had had a psychiatric illness at some time; four more children (0·9 per cent.) had a parent who was referred for psychiatric treatment for the first time during the period when the child attended the Department. The corresponding figures for the 461 patients in 1959 were 84 (18·1 per cent.) and six (1·3 per cent.). The increased number of mentally-ill parents among the 1959 children was in keeping with the known increase in the last few years of adult patients in England and Wales who received psychiatric care (*Registrar General's Statistical Review of England and Wales: Supplement on Mental Health, 1960*). An increase in the number of patients seen also occurred at The Bethlem Royal Hospital and The Maudsley Hospital (*Triennial Statistical Report 1955–7*).

Accordingly, to compare the Maudsley '*disturbed*' group with the matched Dental and Paediatric groups the current year only (1959) was used. It should be remembered that the '*disturbed*' group had an upper age-limit of 13 years when compared with the Dental children and 11 years when compared with the Paediatric children. In the consideration of parents with mental illness, a possible bias might be that the psychiatrist treating the parent recognized disorder in the child and referred him for treatment, when otherwise no referral would have been made. To eliminate this bias, the one child referred by the psychiatrist treating the parent, who otherwise fitted the criteria, was excluded. The groups are compared in TABLES 3.1 and 3.2.

### TABLE 3.1
#### PARENTAL PSYCHIATRIC ILLNESS IN MAUDSLEY AND DENTAL GROUPS

|  | Maudsley group | | Dental group | |
|---|---|---|---|---|
|  | Number | % | Number | % |
| Children with psychiatrically ill parents | 55 | (*19·3*) | 9 | (*6·2*) |
| Total | 259 | | 145 | |

Critical Ratio = 3·36   p<0·001

### TABLE 3.2
#### PARENTAL PSYCHIATRIC ILLNESS IN MAUDSLEY AND PAEDIATRIC GROUPS

|  | Maudsley group | | Paediatric group | |
|---|---|---|---|---|
|  | Number | % | Number | % |
| Children with psychiatrically ill parents | 36 | (*22·6*) | 7 | (*8·75* |

Critical Ratio = 2·604   p<0·01

One in five (19·3 per cent.) of the Maudsley children had a mentally ill parent compared with 6·2 per cent. in the Dental group, and 22·6 per cent. of Maudsley children compared with 8·75 per cent. in the Paediatric group. Both differences are highly significant.

Unfortunately the age distribution of the Paediatric children was so discrepant from that of the Maudsley children that, when they were matched, the numbers were too small for a meaningful comparison of Paediatric sub-groups. Nevertheless, the figures, for what they are worth, do not contradict an association between psychiatric disorder in parents and in their children (4 of 10 children with psychiatric disorder had parents with mental illness as against 3 of 60 with organic disease or no disease and none of the 16 for whom the diagnosis was uncertain).

### Possible Influences of Parental Age

Although the Maudsley, Dental and Paediatric groups had been matched for age and social class, the possibility remained that the difference was an artifact if the parents' ages differed markedly in the groups, even though the children's ages were the same. As psychiatric illness, as defined, referred to psychiatric treatment at any time in the past, an increasing incidence would be expected with a rise in parental age. To test this possible source of bias, the ages of the parents in the groups were compared.

In all three groups, the fathers were about three years older than the mothers and the parents in the Dental and Paediatric groups tended slightly but not uniformly to be older than in the Maudsley groups. The differences between mean ages were not significant for either mothers or fathers and the trend, such as it was, would increase rather than decrease the significance of the greater number of Maudsley children with mentally ill parents.

### Possible Referral Biases

It could be argued that the differences between the Dental and Paediatric, and the Maudsley groups, were artifacts, the parental mental illness having caused a bias towards referral of the children to a psychiatric clinic. 'Mal-adjustment' of various kinds is very common in childhood (Cummings, 1944 and 1946; Lapouse and Monk, 1958 and 1959; Ministry of Education, 1955; Ullman, 1952), and only a proportion of maladjusted children get referred to a psychiatrist. One way of controlling such an artifact would be to examine the rate of parental psychiatic illness among the 'non-disturbed' Maudsley children. The same biases could be expected to operate in children diagnosed as having epilepsy, mental subnormality, organic illness, or 'no psychiatric disorder', where also only a proportion is referred to hospital and not all of this proportion to a psychiatric clinic. Although psychogenic factors may have played a part in this group, it was likely to be markedly less than in the 'disturbed' group. If the difference between groups was 'real', rather than a reflection of referral bias, a similar difference should be found between the '*disturbed*' and '*non-disturbed*' Maudsley groups. Accordingly, the groups were matched for age [TABLE 3.3 in the APPENDIX], but were too small to match for social class, though there was no consistent difference in the gradient of social class between the two groups, and it is later shown that social class was unrelated to the incidence of parental psychiatric illness (within the '*disturbed*' group).

In the '*disturbed*' group 110 children (20·7 per cent.) had mentally ill parents compared with seven (7 per cent.) in the '*non-disturbed*' group. This difference is significant (p<0·01), and confirms that the difference between the Dental and Paediatric and the Maudsley groups was unlikely to be due to referral bias. Comparisons are summarized graphically in FIGURE 3.1.

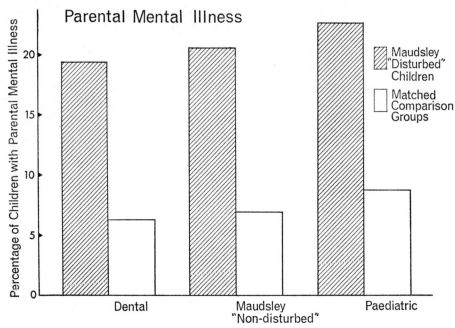

FIG. 3.1. Comparison of the incidence of parental mental illness between Maudsley Hospital child-patients and three comparison groups.

If the presence of a psychiatrically ill parent did cause a bias towards referral of a disturbed child where otherwise no referral would have been made, the disturbance in the child should be milder or of shorter duration than in other children seen in the clinic. To test this possibility the '*disturbed*' group was split into: (1) children with mentally ill parents (the '*psychiatric*' group); (2) children whose parent was referred to a psychiatrist for the first time during the child's treatment (this group was excluded); and (3) children of whom neither parent had had a psychiatric disorder (the '*other*' group). The '*psychiatric*' and '*other*' groups were compared.

The duration of the child's symptoms before his first attendance at the Maudsley was assessed from the records and the children were divided into three groups; those whose symptoms started less than six months before attendance, those whose symptoms started between six months and three years previously, and those whose symptoms had been present for three years or longer. Where data were insufficient to make this assessment the children were excluded for the purposes of comparison. The results are shown in TABLE 3.4.

TABLE 3.4
DURATION OF SYMPTOMS

| | Duration of Symptoms | | | | | | |
|---|---|---|---|---|---|---|---|
| Group | Less than 6 months | | 6 months –3 years | | 3 years or more | | Total | Not known |
| | Number | % | Number | % | Number | % | | Number % |
| Psychiatric | 16 | (13·9) | 51 | (44·4) | 48 | (41·7) | 115 | 22 (16·1) |
| Other | 88 | (17·3) | 228 | (44·8) | 193 | (37·9) | 509 | 83 (14·0) |

Chi square = 1·00  2 d.f.  Not significant

There were no significant differences between the 'psychiatric' and 'other' groups with regard to duration of symptoms before the child's first attendance at the Department. Duration is affected by a number of variables which are to some extent unknown, and is a combination of duration of symptoms before referral and time on the waiting list before being seen. Ideally, only the former period should be used for comparison, but data for this were not always available and the influence of the waiting list could not be measured directly, though it could to some extent be indirectly expressed. Clein (1959) made a study of children who were put on the Maudsley Children's Department waiting list but failed to attend. Non-attendances were compared with the first 100 patients seen in 1955. The only significant difference between the two groups was that non-attenders were on the waiting list twice as long as the attenders before being given an appointment. Consequently, by using non-attenders as a crude measure of length of time on the waiting list, this possible artifact could be estimated. If the duration of symptoms before referral in the 'psychiatric' and 'other' groups was truly different, but this difference was concealed by differences in waiting list time, then there should be a marked difference in rates of parental mental illness between the Maudsley group used in this study (all of whom attended) and Clein's group of non-attenders. Clein did not study this variable, but he has made available his records of non-attenders. As non-attenders included all diagnostic groups and the study was made in 1955, his group was compared with the whole 1955 group of Maudsley children. There was no significant difference between the proportion of mentally-ill parents in the 1955 attenders (14·2 per cent.) and the 1955 non-attenders (11·9 per cent.), and thus no evidence that parental psychiatric illness led to an earlier referral.

To test the possibility that the children of mentally ill parents might be referred for a milder disorder, the 'psychiatric' and 'other' groups were compared in respect of symptoms and number of fields of disturbance shown by the children. 'Severity' of disorder cannot be realistically measured when the estimate of this in a heterogeneous group of conditions depends upon a multitude of variables, including such value-judgements as whether temper tantrums are 'worse' than nocturnal enuresis or depression. No attempt was made to weight symptoms according to any such judgement and, as the data were not adequate for any meaningful grading of symptoms, they were recorded simply as present or absent and a total obtained of the number of symptoms present in each child.

There is no universally agreed categorization of symptoms in child psychiatric disorders and, according to how they are defined, a long or short list of possible symptoms can be obtained. The categorization used was adapted from the one formulated by Cameron (1955). To describe the form of disorder in any child he presented a coherent scheme based on overt symptoms and not depending on any theory of causation. The symptoms were grouped under different headings according to the sphere of disturbance (e.g. 'primary habit disturbance' was a field including disorders of those habits normally acquired by the child—speech, micturition, defaecation, etc., and 'secondary habit disturbance' included such maladaptive habits as nail-biting or head-banging). Cameron did not show these areas to be homogeneous and exception might be taken to some of the groupings. Nevertheless, the scheme has the merit of simplicity and, especially as the Maudsley history-taking is based on it, it seemed to offer the best available approach. Symptoms and fields are listed in the APPENDIX.

All symptoms were judged present or absent according to the information in each child's records. The opinion of the psychiatrist in charge of the case was used to determine whether any symptom was so severe or at such an age as to be regarded as abnormal. Children with a clear-cut neurotic illness of the adult type (e.g. hysteria or obsessional neurosis) were excluded as it was considered that comparison of number of symptoms between a child with neurosis and one with a behaviour disorder would not be meaningful. The use of symptom counts, even with similar disorders, is a rather crude measure of severity of illness. Nevertheless, in the absence of any better criterion, it was considered justifiable. Comparisons between the *psychiatric* and *other* groups are shown in TABLES 3.5 and 3.6.

TABLE 3.5
SEVERITY OF DISORDER IN CHILDREN

| Group | Severity of disorder | | | | | | Total |
|---|---|---|---|---|---|---|---|
| | Mild | | Moderate | | Severe | | |
| | Number | % | Number | % | Number | % | |
| Psychiatric | 37 | (31·9) | 40 | (34·5) | 39 | (33·6) | 116 |
| Other | 230 | (46·6) | 165 | (33·5) | 98 | (19·9) | 493 |

Chi square = 12·57   2 d.f.   p<0·01

KEY:   Mild = 1–6 symptoms
　　　Moderate = 7–9 symptoms
　　　Severe = 10 or more symptoms

TABLE 3.6
EXTENT OF DISORDER IN CHILDREN

*Extent of disorder*

| Group | Slight Number | % | Moderate Number | % | Wide Number | % | Total |
|---|---|---|---|---|---|---|---|
| Psychiatric | 22 | (*19·0*) | 56 | (*48·3*) | 38 | (*32·7*) | 116 |
| Other | 175 | (*35·5*) | 235 | (*47·7*) | 83 | (*16·8*) | 493 |

Chi square = 18·56   2 d.f.   p<0·001

KEY:  Slight   = 1–3 fields
     Moderate = 4–5 fields
     Wide   = 6 or more fields

The children with psychiatrically ill parents had a more severe disturbance (as judged by the number of symptoms) and also a wider disturbance (as judged by the number of fields involved) than the others. Both differences were highly significant. Thus, an artifact of referral for a milder disorder could be definitely excluded, at least as measured in this way. On the contrary, the children were more disturbed.

A further possibility of bias remained. Although there was not a bias towards the psychiatric referral of children of psychiatrically ill parents, there might still be a bias towards the referral of such children to the Maudsley rather than to other hospitals or clinics. As a post-graduate training centre it is likely that The Maudsley Hospital tends to receive a greater proportion of children with more severe disorders than the average child guidance clinic. As such, there may be a greater amount of psychiatric illness among the parents of children attending The Maudsley Hospital because, as has been shown, such illness is commoner among the parents of children with severer disorders. There is no reason to suppose that there was any other referral bias which could have affected the result, but it could not be ruled out in the

TABLE 3.7
REFERRAL AGENCY

*Referral agency*

| Group | 1 No. | % | 2 No. | % | 3 No. | % | 4 No. | % | 5 No. | % | 6 No. | % | Total |
|---|---|---|---|---|---|---|---|---|---|---|---|---|---|
| Psychiatric | 42 | (*30·7*) | 15 | (*10·9*) | 15 | (*10·9*) | 6 | (*4·4*) | 44 | (*32·2*) | 15 | (*10·9*) | 137 |
| Other | 188 | (*31·8*) | 96 | (*16·2*) | 47 | (*7·9*) | 23 | (*3·9*) | 175 | (*29·6*) | 63 | (*10·6*) | 592 |

No significant differences

KEY:  1 = general practitioner
     2 = probation service, remand home or court
     3 = L.C.C. Children's Care Committee or local education authority
     4 = either parent directly
     5 = psychiatric unit, mental hospital, child guidance clinic or private psychiatrist
     6 = miscellaneous, including any non-psychiatric specialist, voluntary organization or other sources

case of children referred by their general practitioners. However, the possibility that the high rate of parental mental illness in the Maudsley group was due to a differential referral of children with mentally ill parents by other psychiatrists and clinics could be tested by comparing the rates of specialist referral in the 'psychiatric' and 'other' groups [TABLE 3.7].

The groups did not differ in the proportions referred by different agencies. There was, therefore, no evidence that cases were particularly referred to The Maudsley Hospital by other specialists because psychiatric illness was present in the children's parents. It may be concluded that the threefold increase in rate of parental psychiatric illness among children below the age of 14 years attending The Maudsley Hospital was not explicable in terms of referral biases.

## II. PARENTAL PHYSICAL ILLNESS IN MAUDSLEY, DENTAL, AND PAEDIATRIC GROUPS

Parental physical illness was considered in the same way as described for parental psychiatric disorders. Comparison between the Maudsley and Dental groups is shown in TABLE 3.8 and that between the Maudsley and Paediatric groups in TABLE 3.9.

### TABLE 3.8
#### PARENTAL PHYSICAL ILLNESS IN MAUDSLEY AND DENTAL GROUPS

| Parental Physical Illness | Maudsley No. % | Dental No. % | Significance p value |
|---|---|---|---|
| None | 145 (56·0) | 87 (60·0) | N.S. |
| Acute illness | 44 (17·0) | 36 (24·8) | N.S. |
| Recurrent illness | 31 (12·0) | 10 (6·9) | <0·1 |
| Chronic illness | 39 (15·1) | 12 (8·3) | <0·06 |
| *Diagnostic Groups* | | | |
| Cardiorespiratory disease | 28 (10·8) | 14 (9·6) | N.S. |
| Gastrointestinal disease | 22 (8·5) | 10 (6·9) | N.S. |
| Disease of joints | 12 (4·6) | 7 (4·8) | N.S. |
| Traumatic disorders | 14 (5·4) | 7 (4·8) | N.S. |
| Gynaecological disease | 14 (5·4) | 4 (2·8) | N.S. |
| Epilepsy | 5 (1·9) | — (—) | N.S. |
| Other neurological disorders | 16 (6·2) | 2 (1·4) | <0·03 |
| Tuberculosis | 6 (2·3) | 3 (2·1) | N.S. |
| Deafness | 7 (2·7) | 1 (0·7) | N.S. |
| Other diseases | 41 (15·8) | 15 (10·3) | N.S. |
| *Recurrent and Chronic Illness only* | | | |
| Both parents ill | 7 (2·7) | 2 (1·4) | |
| Mother only ill | 29 (11·2) | 7 (4·8) | |
| Father only ill | 34 (13·1) | 13 (8·9) | |
| Total Children | 259 | 145 | |

TABLE 3.9

PARENTAL PHYSICAL ILLNESS IN MAUDSLEY AND PAEDIATRIC GROUPS

| Parental Physical Illness | Maudsley No. % | Paediatric No. % | Significance p value |
|---|---|---|---|
| None | 96 (60·3) | 53 (66·25) | N.S. |
| Acute illness | 23 (15·1) | 18 (22·50) | N.S. |
| Recurrent illness | 19 (12·0) | 4 (5·00) | } <0·02 |
| Chronic illness | 21 (12·6) | 5 (6·25) | |
| | | | |
| *Diagnostic Groups* | | | |
| Cardiorespiratory disease | 14 (8·8) | 8 (10·00) | N.S. |
| Gastrointestinal disease | 13 (8·2) | 2 (2·50) | N.S. |
| Disease of joints | 7 (4·4) | 4 (5·00) | N.S. |
| Traumatic disorders | 6 (3·8) | 3 (3·75) | N.S. |
| Gynaecological disorders | 5 (3·1) | 1 (1·25) | N.S. |
| Epilepsy | 5 (3·1) | 1 (1·25) | N.S. |
| Other neurological disorders | 10 (6·3) | 2 (2·50) | N.S. |
| Tuberculosis | 5 (3·1) | 1 (1·25) | N.S. |
| Deafness | 4 (2·5) | 1 (1·25) | N.S. |
| Other diseases | 26 (16·4) | 8 (10·00) | N.S. |
| | | | |
| *Recurrent and Chronic Illness only* | | | |
| Both parents ill | 4 (2·5) | | |
| Mother only ill | 17 (10·7) | 7 (8·75) | |
| Father only ill | 19 (12·0) | 2 (2·50) | |
| | | | |
| Total children | 159 | 80 | |

The overall proportion of children with one or more physically ill parents did not differ between the Maudsley and Dental groups, but both recurrent and chronic illnesses were in excess among the parents of children attending the psychiatric department, 12·0 per cent. and 15·1 per cent. respectively as against 6·9 per cent. and 8·3 per cent. in the Dental group. These differences fell just short of statistical significance but when recurrent and chronic illness were combined, comparison of the groups produced a critical ratio of 2·6 which was significant ($p<0·01$). If only parents with recurrent or chronic illness were taken the groups did not differ on which parent was ill [TABLE 3.8]. The overall distribution of diagnostic groups was also similar, except for a probably significant excess of parents with neurological disease in the Maudsley group (C.R. = 2·24, $p<0·03$).

Comparison of the Maudsley and Paediatric groups produced similar findings [TABLE 3.9]. Recurrent and chronic physical disorders were significantly more frequent among the parents of children attending the Psychiatric Department, 24·6 per cent. as against 11·25 per cent. in the Paediatric group ($p<0·02$). Neurological disorders were less in excess than in the first comparison and the difference was not significant.

To check for referral biases the '*disturbed*' and '*non-disturbed*' sub-groups of children attending the Maudsley were also compared for physical disorder in the parents [TABLE 3.10]. A quarter of the '*disturbed*' children (25·4 per cent.) had parents with a chronic or recurrent disorder compared with only one in nine (11·0 per cent.) of the '*non-disturbed*' children with organic and other disorders. Neurological disease was only insignificantly in excess but gastrointestinal disease and 'other disease' were both significantly more frequent among parents of the '*disturbed*' children.

TABLE 3.10
PARENTAL PHYSICAL ILLNESS IN DISTURBED AND
NON-DISTURBED GROUPS

| Parental Physical Illness | Disturbed No. % | Non-disturbed No. % | Significance p value |
|---|---|---|---|
| None | 325 (*61·1*) | 74 (*74·0*) | <0·01 |
| Acute illness | 73 (*13·7*) | 15 (*15·0*) | N.S. |
| Recurrent illness | 68 (*12·8*) | 5 (*5·0*) | } <0·01 |
| Chronic illness | 67 (*12·6*) | 6 (*6·0*) | |
| *Diagnostic Groups* | | | |
| Cardiorespiratory disease | 43 (*8·1*) | 6 (*6·0*) | N.S. |
| Gastrointestinal disease | 37 (*7·0*) | 1 (*1·0*) | <0·03 |
| Disease of joints | 17 (*3·2*) | — (—) | — |
| Traumatic disorders | 20 (*3·7*) | 2 (*2·0*) | N.S. |
| Gynaecological disorders | 27 (*5·1*) | 7 (*7·0*) | N.S. |
| Epilepsy | 10 (*1·9*) | 2 (*2·0*) | } N.S. |
| Other neurological disorders | 21 (*3·8*) | — (—) | |
| Tuberculosis | 19 (*3·6*) | 4 (*4·0*) | N.S. |
| Deafness | 11 (*2·1*) | 1 (*1·0*) | N.S. |
| Other diseases | 74 (*13·9*) | 3 (*3·0*) | <0·01 |
| *Recurrent and Chronic Illness only* | | | |
| Both parents ill | 11 (*2·1*) | 1 (*1·0*) | |
| Mother only ill | 66 (*12·4*) | 5 (*5·0*) | |
| Father only ill | 58 (*10·9*) | 5 (*5·0*) | |
| Total children | 532 | 100 | |

Thus, in all three comparisons, the parents of children with psychiatric disorders showed a significant excess of recurrent and chronic illness suggesting, as this was also found in the comparison within the Maudsley group of '*disturbed*' and '*non-disturbed*' children, that the excess was not due to referral bias. However, there was not a significant deficiency of healthy parents in the Maudsley group compared with the Dental and Paediatric groups. The excess of chronic and recurrent illness was partially compensated for by a paucity of parents with acute illness (although the last difference did not reach significance). It seemed, therefore, not that there was an excess of illness but that illnesses were more often chronic. On the other hand, when '*disturbed*' and '*non-disturbed*' children within the Maudsley population were compared, there were significantly fewer parents without illness in the '*disturbed*' group (p <0·01) and the proportion with acute illness was similar in the two groups. As information regarding Maudsley children was culled from hospital records, and not from interviews, as in the Dental and Paediatric groups, acute parental illnesses may not always have been recorded. (For instance, some illnesses fulfilling the criteria for acute illness were relatively minor disorders.) Whether or not this was so, there was certainly a significant excess of chronic and recurrent physical illness among parents of children with neurotic or behaviour disorders attending The Maudsley Hospital.

The possibility that parental physical illness led to the more ready referral of the mildly ill child was examined in the same way as it had been for parental mental illness. When children with parents who had chronic recurrent physical illness were compared with the remainder of the clinic population there were no sizeable or significant differences with regard to duration and number of symptoms, or number of fields of disturbance. The groups were therefore closely comparable in duration, severity and extent of child psychiatric disorder.

Out of 30 comparisons of the distribution of diagnostic groups, only three differences reached statistical significance and no difference was found in all three comparisons. Diagnosis was thus probably not very relevant in this connection. Nevertheless, neurological disorders and 'other diseases' were more frequent, although not always significantly so, in the Maudsley '*disturbed*' group in each comparison. Both categories contained a disproportionately large number of illnesses which had lasted over a year and the 'other diseases' group contained a high number of fatal illnesses (carcinoma of the breast, renal disorders, etc.). When the group with recurrent and chronic illness was split according to which parent was ill, the numbers were small, no consistent differences were found, and no excess of physical illness was found more in one parent than in the other.

*Association between Psychiatric Disorder and Chronic or Recurrent Physical Illness*

The next step was to see to what extent physical and mental illness was associated. Children with a physically ill parent were no more likely to have a mentally ill parent than were other children attending the Maudsley but there was an association between the two types of illness. When children who had both a parent with physical illness and one with mental illness were considered both types of disorder were found to occur in the *same* parent to a probably significant extent (p<0·04). Altogether 30 children had parents one of whom had a chronic or recurrent physical illness and one of whom had a mental illness. In 19 cases both illnesses occurred in the same parent, whereas in only 11 cases did they occur in different parents.

*Discussion and Summary*

Of children with a psychiatric disorder attending The Maudsley Hospital, one in five had a mentally ill parent. This incidence was three times that in closely matched groups of children attending Dental and Paediatric clinics. The proportion with mentally ill parents in a matched group of children attending The Maudsley Hospital for *non-psychiatric* disorder (epilepsy, organic illness etc.) was similar to that in the Dental and Paediatric populations, and significantly less than the proportion found in children attending for *psychiatric* disorders. Thus there appeared no disproportionate tendency to refer children with mentally ill parents to a psychiatric hospital. Nor was there reason to suppose that the presence of a mentally ill parent led to referral earlier, or for lesser disorders. Indeed, the children with mentally ill parents had more severe and extensive disorders than other children at the same clinic, as noted by Koch (1939), the duration of symptoms was similar in the two groups, and children whose parents had psychiatric disorders were referred from the same agencies as other children.

It seems clear that in the population studied, there was a marked and highly significant excess of parental psychiatric illness, and the question arises: How far can the finding in this group be generalized? There have been no previous systematic studies of the incidence of parental illness among children attending a psychiatric clinic, but several writers have commented on the high rates of parental mental illness among clinic children and there is some evidence of increased rates of psychiatric disorder among the children of neurotic or psychopathic parents. So, the present investigation does provide some substance for the impressions of earlier writers.

A more fundamental problem is the relationship of these findings to the association between psychiatric illness in the parent and child in the general population. Caution must always be exercised in generalizing from studies in selected hospital populations. Although the evidence suggests that referral bias did not operate in this study, other possible sources of bias remain. Berkson (1946) has shown that, for statistical reasons separate from referral biases, the ratio of multiple diagnoses to single diagnoses in hospital will always be greater than in the general population. This artifact is found in associations between conditions where only a small proportion of each is referred to hospital. The situation in the present study is rather different, but where family problems may be dealt with by referral either of the child or of the parent to hospital, a similar effect may have operated to produce a spuriously high association of hospital-treated illnesses between different members of the same family. However, it is unlikely that this could have created any sizeable bias. More important, general population studies support the present findings. In a careful and well planned epidemiological study, Buck and Laughton (1959) found a significant association between psychiatric disorder in parents and children in a Canadian town, and two recent

British studies (Kellner, 1963; Hare and Shaw, 1965) also provide confirmatory findings. Further studies of hospital groups and general populations are required but the work to date suggests that the findings of the present investigation are not confined to the population of a particular hospital, but may be generalized to a wider group.

The incidence of chronic and recurrent parental physical illness was also significantly raised among Maudsley children, being twice that in matched groups of children attending Paediatric and Dental clinics. The total rate of parental physical illness did not differ significantly between these groups, but as it did differ between children attending the Maudsley for *psychiatric* and those attending for *non-psychiatric* disorders, the relative deficit of acute parental physical illness in the group of Maudsley children might be due to under-recording. There was no tendency for the excess of illness to be accounted for by any particular diagnostic categories, although neurological disorders were somewhat more frequent in the parents of psychiatrically ill children. Referral biases were not found.

Several studies, epidemiological and clinical, have noted associations between parental physical illness or incapacity and psychiatric disorder in the children but none is entirely satisfactory. The problems for the children associated with a parent's admission to hospital have been well described (Ekdahl et al., 1962) and doubtless this is an important consequence of some chronic parental illnesses. Further work is needed to delineate the association between parental physical illness and psychiatric disorder in the children but the evidence suggests that the association may not be confined to the population of the present study.

The finding that the association with disorder in the child is not restricted to mental illness in the parent but includes all chronic or recurrent illness is important, and suggests that consideration of the effects of parental illness on the children should extend beyond the direct effects of parental morbid behaviour or attitudes. When parental physical and mental illness were both present, they were more likely to occur in the *same* parent than in different parents. Thus there was a significant association between physical and mental disorders in the parents.

In part, the relevance for the child of chronic physical illness in the parent may be through this association of physical and psychiatric disorders. Physical illnesses have been found to occur more frequently among psychiatric patients than healthy controls (Doust, 1952; Roessler and Greenfield, 1961), and in an epidemiological study Longaker and Godden (1960) found that individuals with a relatively large number of organic symptoms tended also to be rated high on psychiatric symptoms. Studies of the illness experience of various groups of adults have demonstrated that people reporting a greater number of bodily illnesses were also more likely to report disturbance of mood, thought, and behaviour (Hinkle and Wolff, 1957; Hinkle, 1959).

Psychiatric variables may also influence the outcome of purely physical disease. Scores on psychological tests have been shown to be related to the time of recovery from acute respiratory infections (Brodman *et al.*, 1947), from surgical operations (Schneider *et al.*, 1950), and from infectious mononucleosis (Greenfield *et al.*, 1959). A relationship with the rate of growth of tumours has even been claimed (Blumberg *et al.*, 1954; Klopfer, 1957) although this was not confirmed by Krasnoff (1959). Psychosocial factors have been found to relate to the course of tuberculosis (Holmes *et al.*, 1961) and the presence of affective symptoms to the persistence of peptic ulcer symptoms (Rutter 1963b). Querido (1959) found a significant relationship between 'psychosocial distress' and a low incidence of recovery from most physical illnesses. Ferguson and MacPhail (1954) showed that patients in unsatisfactory social conditions were more likely to remain ill for longer periods than those in better conditions; more illnesses became chronic and more recurred. So there is evidence from a number of sources that people with physical illness are also more likely to have psychiatric disorder, and if they do, the physical disorder is more likely to be chronic or recurrent.

Apart from those who had received formal psychiatric care, a number of parents with chronic or recurrent physical illness had had mental disorder of some severity (one mother had been psychotic for many months), and many more had had lesser disorders of mood and behaviour. These mental disturbances associated with some longstanding physical illnesses may have been an important element in the adverse impact of the parental disorder on the child.

# CHAPTER IV

# BEREAVEMENT IN CHILDHOOD: REVIEW OF THE LITERATURE

ALTHOUGH most parental deaths are a result of an often prolonged illness, the effects on the child have usually been considered only in terms of the separation or loss that death entails. Little has been written on the resulting family changes and even less on how these affect the child. Gardner (1956) compared separation reactions to grief reactions, and Bowlby (1960, 1961a and b), a leading theorist on the effects of parent-child separation, considers that the sequence of responses to separation (which he describes as protest, despair, and detachment) is characteristic of all forms of mourning. However, although separation has been regarded as a form of bereavement, and adverse reactions to separation have been 'explained' as due to grief, the relationship between parental death and child psychiatric disorder has not been systematically studied. Most statistical investigations have been concerned with death only as a cause of a 'broken home'. However, because of the dearth of studies specifically related to parental death, some of the literature concerning 'broken homes' and the related question of parent-child separations will be surveyed briefly before passing to studies directly concerned with bereavement.

## 'Broken Homes'

The literature on 'broken homes' is so vast that a few key studies will be discussed to represent the variety of relevant investigations. Where available, the figures for parental deaths will be specifically mentioned.

Many workers have noted among delinquents a high rate of 'broken homes', now generally accepted as a causal factor in delinquency, but for the most part institutional children were studied and the 'broken home' may have been as much a 'cause' of the institutionalization as of the delinquency. As the term has often been used loosely and little is known about the frequency of 'broken homes' in the general population, it is difficult to judge to what extent it may be an aetiological agent (Wootton, 1959). Moreover, divorce, separation, or desertion may sometimes be related to deficiencies and abnormalities in parental personalities, and these defects, rather than the 'broken homes' may then constitute the relevant variables.

In many ways the best controlled study was that of the Gluecks (Glueck, S. and Glueck, E., 1950) [already discussed in CHAPTER I] who found significantly fewer delinquents living with their two natural parents, though the difference was largely accounted for by the excess of fathers absent from home through desertion, separation, or divorce. There had been more parental deaths (among delinquents 14·4 per cent. of the fathers and 8 per cent. of the mothers had died as against 12 per cent. and 3·4 per cent. respectively among the non-delinquent children) but these were chiefly due to mothers who had died after the child reached five years.

Burt (1925) also found an excess of maternal, but not paternal, deaths. Of his delinquent children 13·7 per cent. of the mothers had died, compared with a control figure of 4·0 per cent. Although Burt did not remark on the finding, more of the girls (19·0 per cent.) than boys (10·6 per cent.) had lost their mothers. This sex-link is noteworthy in view of Barry and Lindemann's similar finding (1960) for adult neurotics. Although apparently well matched, Burt's control group must be suspect, in view of his abnormally low figures for illegitimacy (0·7 per cent.) and fathers absent through desertion, divorce, or separation (0·2 per cent.).

The importance of 'broken homes' in the genesis of delinquency is called in question by the McCords (1959) who examined outcome in the children who had been assessed earlier as part of the Cambridge-Somerville study. Background factors were rated without knowledge of the child's later career and children who became delinquent were compared with those who did not. Although 'broken homes' had precipitated many men into criminality, few had records of juvenile delinquency. Apparently, quarrelsome and neglecting homes were more conducive to delinquency than 'broken homes'.

In a child guidance clinic study, Holman (1953) found that children 'ascertained' as maladjusted came from 'broken homes' more often than other children at the same clinic. Among the 'ascertained' children 10 homes had been broken by death compared with six in the remainder. Banister and Ravden (1944 and 1945) compared children at a child guidance clinic with 'normal' children from the same schools. Of 112 clinic children, 45 came from broken homes as against 12 in the control group of 93; the difference was significant. There was an excess of parental deaths, 15 compared with 7, but most homes were broken for other reasons and in these parental instability was often an important factor leading to separation. Broken homes were associated more with delinquency than with neurotic disorders.

Wardle (1961) found that children at a child guidance clinic who came from broken homes or who had been separated from their mother tended to show antisocial conduct disorders rather than neurotic symptoms, and the incidence of conduct disorders was as high in children from broken homes who remained with their mother throughout childhood as in those who had been separated temporarily or permanently. Thus, separation itself was not the important factor; separation and disruption of the home both tended to result in adverse child-rearing experiences and hence in disordered conduct. Similarly *mothers* who themselves had come from a broken home tended to have children with conduct disorders even when the child's home was intact and he had never been separated from his mother. Unfortunately, the different causes for break-up of the home were not considered separately. Although broken homes may be particularly associated with conduct disorders, Burt and Howard (1952) found in a study of maladjusted children (from whom delinquents had been expressly excluded), that 12·8 per cent. of fathers and 15·3 per cent. of mothers were dead or absent compared with 4·4 per cent. and 3·1 per cent. respectively in the control group.

Bennett (1960) compared 50 'delinquent' and 50 'neurotic' children in a rural English child guidance clinic. There had been nine parental deaths among the delinquents compared with four among the neurotics. In homes 'broken' from all causes, the numbers were greater, the ratio was similar, and the difference significant. Silverman (1935) studied 138 children placed by an agency because of break-up of the home for reasons other than the child's behaviour (in 50 cases because of parental ill-health or death): 75 per cent. of the children were entirely normal, that is in many cases break-up of the home was compatible with psychiatric normality in the children. Longitudinal studies have also shown that most children from 'broken homes' appear to have developed normally, although rather more had behavioural abnormalities than children from 'normal' homes [see below]. Other studies of delinquents (reviewed by Wootton, 1959) mostly found a high incidence of 'broken homes', although the investigations often had methodological deficiencies.

To summarize the evidence, although probably most children from broken homes are normal, among delinquent or maladjusted children there is unduly often a background of disruption of the home. Disruption because of parental separation or divorce may be somewhat more important than disruption as a result of death, although deaths too are considerably more frequent than expected. Break-up of the home may be less important than the factors which lead to the 'break-up' and less so also than unhappy and discordant homes which have not 'broken'. In so far as they are relevant, 'broken homes' tend more often to lead to delinquency than to neurosis in the child. The consequences of 'break-up' because of death have not been specifically studied.

*Parent-Child Separation*

Separation has usually been considered as part of 'parental deprivation', a subject recently extensively reviewed (Ainsworth, 1962; Casler, 1961; Yarrow, 1961), but whether the effects of deprivation of parental care without separation and separation without deprivation of care are similar remains in doubt, as most studies have been concerned with situations involving both deprivation and separation. Also, many studies of 'maternal deprivation', which have mostly been based on children in institutions, are less informative on the effects of separation than over the quality and quantity of care provided for institutional children.

In 1952, Bowlby produced an extensive review of *maternal* deprivation
D

on behalf of the World Health Organization. Although he did not regard separation as the only form of deprivation, he concluded that mother-child separation during early childhood, even for relatively short periods, usually had serious consequences for the child. Detailed criticisms of this view have been presented by O'Connor (O'Connor, 1956; O'Connor and Franks, 1960); and Bowlby himself, in the light of results not available in 1952, has agreed that in the past the case was overstated (Bowlby et al., 1956).

Early studies on children admitted to institutions (Goldfarb, 1943; Lowrey, 1940; Spitz, 1946), residential nurseries (Burlingham and Freud, 1942 and 1944), and to hospital (Edelston, 1943) found many seriously disturbed children, and highlighted the often appalling patterns of institutional upbringing and the frequent indifference to children's personal relationships and emotional requirements.

Later studies (Bowlby, 1953; Heinicke, 1956; Illingworth and Holt, 1955; Woodward, 1959) confirmed these findings, but Prugh et al. (1953) showed that daily visiting and improved ward conditions reduced the frequency and severity of the emotional disturbances. Such disturbances were most marked in the pre-school child (Prugh et al., 1953) but rarely occurred in infants under six months (Schaffer and Callender, 1959) and were not invariably present at any age (Schaffer, 1958). Sklarew (1959) showed that the effects of separation differed in boys and girls, and Stott (1956) and Howells and Layng (1955) demonstrated that although sometimes leading to psychiatric disorder, separation from their mothers in early childhood was compatible with normal development in many children. Lewis (1954), too, in her study of deprived children, found that only lasting separation before the age of two years had much relationship with later psychiatric abnormality; the circumstances of separation were more important than separation itself.

These findings have been broadly confirmed by prospective and 'follow-up' studies. In children in a sanatorium, and so separated from their parents during the first four years of life, Bowlby and his associates (1956) found that the outcome was diverse and that many of the children were well-adjusted, though they did show disturbed behaviour somewhat more frequently than a control group of the same age and sex in the same class at school.

The prospective study of Newcastle infants failed to demonstrate any significant correlation between break-up of the home and disorder in the children (Miller et al., 1960), but, so far, the children have been observed only during early childhood. Of children studied in the National Survey, in which a nationally representative sample of children has been followed from birth, those separated from a parent in the first four years but remaining at home, showed no evidence of increased emotional instability, but those who were separated from their parents and away from home (Douglas and Blomfield, 1958), had an increased incidence of nightmares and habit disturbances, although ill-effects seemed to be confined to the children of non-manual workers (Rowntree, 1955). Children's emotional development was not the prime concern of the study, which gathered only limited information on this aspect, and results referred only to the first five years of life, but later data appear to confirm that the association is confined to middle class families (Douglas, 1961).

Children separated from their homes not infrequently show short-term emotional disturbance, which is probably greatest between the ages of 6 months and 5 years. The disturbance can be much reduced by attention to the care that the child receives, and observation of the later development of children who have experienced separation has shown that many subsequently have normal behaviour, personalities and adjustment, although psychiatric disorder, sometimes serious, has followed separation in others. What qualities of the separation from home are harmful in their effects and what distinguishes those children who suffer from separation from those who are unimpaired by the experience remain matters for speculation. Although separation experiences are usually viewed in terms of maternal deprivation, where the consequences have been maladaptive the children have usually been in some institution, or else in many instances separated from the father as well, and there are no reliable data to show that separation from the one parent is more harmful than from the other.

The work to date suggests that in examining the mode of action of effects of parental death (or separation of parent and child because of parental illness), emphasis should be placed on the ways in which the care of the children (emotional as well as physical) is impaired rather than on the fact of separation. What qualities of care are most important is still a matter of dispute. Harriet Rheingold's (1956) investigations of infants suggest that the mere amount of attention given to the child is important. Studies of 'working' mothers (Yudkin and Holme, 1963) and of Kibbutzim children (Rabin, 1957, 1958, and 1959; Spiro, 1955) have demonstrated that 'multiple mothering' is not necessarily harmful, although frequent changes and gross discontinuity of care may be (Moore, 1963). Perceptual deprivation may also play a role (Casler, 1961). Bowlby (1961a and b), in particular, has sought to integrate the effects of separation with what is known from investigations of animal behaviour. There is evidence that animals have a 'need' for companionship (usually supplied by the parent) and that this need is independent of feeding (Rollman-Branch, 1960). However, the instinctual basis implied by the term 'need' is probably incorrect. Recent studies have emphasized the importance of learning in even quite stereotyped species-typical behaviours (see, for example, Bridger, 1962; Lehrman, 1953; Schneirla, 1959; Thorpe, 1961). Harlow has shown the importance of soft body contact in the development of infant monkeys and his ingenious studies have gone some way to demonstrate which aspects of such contact are important and how long the effects last (Harlow, 1958, 1960, 1961; Harlow and Zimmerman, 1959). Similar factors may also be important for human infants, although experimental data are lacking. Parental pathology and other abnormalities in the situation that led to separation are also important (Hirsch, 1937), separation from the child's parents may be harmful, but may also be beneficial, if the parent-child relationship is sufficiently grossly disturbed. The aspects of the relationship which are important for the normal development of the child have only begun to be explored.

## Bereavement

The literature on the subject of bereavement has been well reviewed by Parkes (1962 and 1964). Abraham (1911) first pointed out the similarities between grief and depression, and Freud (1917) related mourning and melancholia as aspects of the same process. Lindemann (1944), from a study of 101 patients, maintained that, '. . . acute grief is a definite syndrome with psychological and somatic symptomatology'. The chief features he described were: somatic distress, preoccupation with the image of the deceased, guilt, hostile reactions, and loss of patterns of conduct. A further feature was the appearance in the bereaved person of symptoms shown by the deceased in his last illness. Murray (1937) and Fenichel (1945) also commented on this. Parkes (1964) has shown that illnesses after the death of a near relative were significantly more likely to be neurotic or reactive depressive disorders than illnesses not associated with bereavement.

Marris (1958) made a careful study of 72 London women who had been widowed in the preceding four years; they sometimes took two years or more to become reconciled to the bereavement. Symptoms shown by these women (who were not patients) were similar to those described by Lindemann in the mentally ill, except that guilt was less common. Withdrawal and apathy were usual and hostility was present in a third. Half the women had experienced at some time a pronounced sense of the presence of their dead husband.

Volkart (1957) discussed attitudes to bereavement in different cultures, and pointed out that in the 'small family' system of Western society there tend to develop strong emotional ties, sometimes with over-identification and over-dependence. The loss of a family member is often more serious than in cultures where there are less exclusive emotional attachments and where roles tend to be more important than the people playing them. Waller (1951) made the same point: '. . . One of the prices we pay for intimate response in families is painful adjustment to separation, be it by conscription, divorce, or death'. Also, the social role in our culture, unlike some others, makes no real provision for dealing with emotions other than love (for example, hostility and guilt) (Volkart, 1957).

Psychoanalysts have stressed that the presence of undue ambivalence about the dead person much complicates mourning and may lead to pathological development (Freud, 1917; Fenichel, 1945; Waller, 1951). The evidence is clinical and open to criticism, but certainly ambivalence has appeared as a prominent feature in many of the published cases and is in keeping with evidence from social anthropology.

Waller (1951) compared the features of family relationships which seem to determine reactions to bereavement with those found relevant to reactions to other crises. Family adaptability, family integration, family affection, good marital adjustment of husband and wife, and companionable parent-child relationships were associated with satisfactory adjustment to wartime separations (Reuben Hill, 1949). Similar factors may be important in relation to family deaths.

## The Child's Concept of Death

It is important to distinguish between a child's reactions to the death itself and to its consequences. Studies of child development in Switzerland (Piaget, 1929, 1930, and 1932), Hungary (Nagy, 1948), America (Gesell and Ilg, 1946), and England (Anthony, 1940) all agree that up to the age of about three years, the child has little or no concept of death. The studies, although based on very different theoretical backgrounds, relied on similar data. Children of different ages were asked to give the meaning of 'dead' in the course of a vocabulary list, detailed home records were available, written compositions, discussions and drawings were used, and careful observations were made on the child's use of the terms 'death', 'dead', etc., both spontaneously and in response to formal tests.

The child's ideas of death at different ages reflect his general picture of the world, physical causality, language and thought, and are an aspect of his physiological and psychological maturation. At the age of about four to five years, death tends to be viewed as a departure, perhaps temporary, and is sometimes equated with going to hospital. Death may be personified, and is often closely bound up with beliefs in the omnipotence of thoughts and wishes. At this stage animism is characteristic: everything is endowed with a purpose. Questions on accidents and death are prominent about the age of six to seven years (Piaget, 1932) and at this time the concept of death is puzzling and inexplicable. Fortuity is not understood, things are thought of as causal, as being due to a 'maker', God, parents, etc. An adult concept of death probably does not develop until a few years later.

Mourning in infancy was an integral part of the theoretical framework of the late Melanie Klein, who described the 'infantile depressive position' in relation to weaning (Klein, 1934), and considered that the infant mourned the loss of its mother's breast and blamed itself for the loss which it believed to have resulted from its own greed and destructive fantasies. She held the view that this state was associated with anxiety, guilt, and grief, and that mourning and depression in later life were a reactivation of the infantile depressive position. The evidence for these theories is not scientifically acceptable and the application of adult concepts to infancy seems developmentally unjustifiable.

*Children's Reaction to Bereavement*

Observations on bereaved children are few, and the data are meagre. The most systematic study was that of Marris (1958). He described children's reactions to paternal death as follows: '. . . Some became violently hysterical and cried for weeks afterwards; some refused to speak of their father or hear him mentioned; or they became withdrawn and unsociable. Others showed extraordinary self-possession. Many especially of the younger children did not seem to react at all. . . . The widows were nearly always more deeply and lastingly affected by grief than their children. Only in a few unhappy marriages did the children seem more disturbed by bereavement, either because their father had shown them more affection than he had shown his wife, or because they were more troubled by a sense of guilt'. Burlingham and Freud (1942, 1944), in their description of children's reactions to wartime deaths, stated that the emotional disturbance, although sometimes vigorous, was usually short-lived and, in general, the grief of children was milder and of shorter duration than in adults.

Fenichel (1945) thought that children react to the loss of a loved object by being flooded with libidinal strivings which may lead to panic. They were less able to control the flood of strivings than were adults. The dissolution of ties with the lost object constituted the 'work of mourning' which regulates the depth and duration of the grief reaction. It is not clear whether he implies that the reaction is more severe in children or whether it is shorter-lived because less controlled, and the basis for his statements is not given. Deutsch (1937), on the other hand, maintained that children frequently displayed indifference after death of a loved person and she regarded this 'absence of grief' as likely to lead to pathological development. In a study of normal adults who had lost a parent during childhood, Hilgard (Hilgard *et al.*, 1960) found that grief was recalled only if the death had occurred after the child reached nine years. She also thought that younger children reacted primarily to the grief of the surviving parent, rather than to the death itself.

Arthur and Kemme (1964) investigated in 83 emotionally disturbed children and their families the children's reactions to the death of a parent and found a high incidence of intellectual and emotional problems directly or indirectly related to the loss. Some children felt abandoned, but many experienced only a feeling of hopelessness. Phobic reactions closely related to death occurred in just under half the children. The long term reactions were complex and varied.

*Consequences of Bereavement for the Child*

In the early stages of bereavement, the widow's reaction is sometimes manifested by indifference to her children's needs (Marris, 1958). Poverty and loneliness for the widow often follow the husband's death and play an important role in forcing readjustments (Marris, 1958; Waller, 1951).

For the child as well as for the adult, cultural factors are important. In communities where emotional attachments are less exclusive than in the Western world, the death of a parent creates fewer problems for children, but in this country, bereavement necessarily leads to adjustments in family attitudes and an alteration of roles (Waller, 1951). Alterations in contact with relatives also occur; impaired relationships with the deceased husband's family frequently followed his death in the widows studied by Marris (1958).

In Hilgard's study of adults bereaved in childhood, she contrasted those reasonably well adjusted with those who were emotionally disturbed (Hilgard and Newman, 1959; Hilgard et al., 1960). Factors which appeared important in aiding successful adjustment to bereavement in childhood were: (1) a compatible relationship, with a definition of roles between the parents before death; (2) a strong surviving parent who accepts his or her dual role with courage and a minimum of conflict; (3) a network of family and/or community resources which the parent is able to use; (4) the development of a separation tolerance before the death of a parent through the whole series of separations involved in the course of psycho-sexual development. The dependence of the surviving parent, particularly the mother, upon the growing children sometimes affected the degree of maturity the children achieved in close inter-personal relationships later in life. Marris (1958) also found that children, especially boys, even when young, tended to take their deceased father's place in the home and sometimes found it difficult to reconcile their adult role at home with their child's role at school. He thought that if widows were over-dependent on their sons, there might be later difficulties when the sons wished to achieve independence. Waller (1951) made similar observations.

Mourning for the loss of a parent of the opposite sex was described by English and Pearson (1937) but they regarded the loss of the same-sexed parent as more harmful. 'The loss of the parent of the same sex imposes a still heavier burden. In the midst of a death-wish towards his father, the little boy suddenly finds his wishes come true. Thus his belief in the omnipotence of his wishes becomes justified by fate. His wishes become dangerous weapons.' Such a view would not be dissonant with the findings of developmental studies (Piaget, 1930, 1932; Anthony, 1940) that up to the age of five years, the child tends to give magical explanations for occurrences, things being thought of as happening for a purpose, often through the omnipotence of the child's thought or wishes. However, these data would not necessarily support the view of English and Pearson (1937) that the loss is most serious during the period of four to seven years, at the height of the Oedipus situation. English and Pearson also stated, as has Neubauer (1960), that parental death leads to serious interference with the normal course of psychosexual development. The child is left highly sensitized to disappointment, and tends to be more than usually susceptible to later libidinal losses. This view seems to adumbrate Hilgard's more recent work on 'anniversary reactions' (Hilgard and Newman, 1959), when adult grief reactions were linked with reactions to parental death in childhood.

Remarriage of the surviving parent both ameliorates and aggravates the situation. Marris (1958) found that remarriage eased the plight of many widows by relieving poverty and loneliness, although few of the marriages were regarded by the widows as being as satisfactory as the first. The step-fathers were often resented by the widows' children and widows with children were less likely to remarry than those who were childless (Marris, 1958; Waller, 1951). Janet (1925) described the disorders in children which followed the entry into the household of a widow's relatives or a widower's mistress; these factors accentuated the child's work of adaptation after bereavement.

The difficulties for the child associated with remarriage of the surviving parent have received particular attention from Heilpern (1943) and Podolsky (1955). Heilpern emphasized that the arrival of a step-parent was an additional trauma on top of previous bereavement, the trauma operating through reactivation of the Oedipus situation. She stated that this was only one factor; all children are not affected and dispositional and constitutional factors are also important. Podolsky believed that the problems associated with the addition of a new family tie were particularly difficult at adolescence when there is a clash with the onset of striving for individuality and independence. There are the difficulties of comparisons with the departed parent, jealousies associated with the affection of the true parent for the new spouse and later accentuations of sibling rivalry, especially in relation to half-sibs.

This brief review indicates that the consequences for the child are complex, but that there are, as yet, not enough data upon which to build any coherent theory of reactions to bereavement. The effects on the child are probably as much a function of what happens before as of what happens after the death. The immediate reactions probably depend on the cultural setting, the age of the child, the sexes of the child and parent, previous personality variables and family relationships, to mention but a few. Although bereavement may necessitate major readjustments, many children develop normally after bereavement and statistical associations between bereavement and child psychiatric disorders have still to be established.

# CHAPTER V

# INCIDENCE OF PARENTAL DEATHS

As an important consequence of physical illness, parental deaths were considered separately. When the groups were compared the rate of parental deaths was higher among the children attending the Psychatric Department than among those attending either Dental or Paediatric Clinics [TABLE 5.1]. The rate was also higher among the *'disturbed'* than among the *'non-disturbed'* children, but in all groups the numbers were too small for reliable comparisons.

TABLE 5.1
PARENTAL DEATHS IN DIFFERENT GROUPS

| Children | Maudsley No. % | Dental No. % |
|---|---|---|
| Bereaved children | 21 *(8·1)* | 2 *(1·4)* |
| Total children | 259 | 145 |
| | Maudsley No. % | Paediatric No. % |
| Bereaved children | 9 *(5·7)* | 2 *(2·5)* |
| Total children | 159 | 80 |
| | Maudsley disturbed No. % | Non-disturbed No. % |
| Bereaved children | 51 *(9·6)* | 6 *(6·0)* |
| Total children | 532 | 100 |

A problem that has bedevilled other studies of rates of parental death in various diagnostic groups has been the difficulty of finding a suitable population with which to compare the group being investigated. When the factor (such as parental death) occurs in only a few of the subjects, large numbers are essential, but it is not enough for the groups to be large. Certain variables which affect rates of death are known and if these are not equated in the population studied, gross discrepancies can arise. Before proceeding to the method of comparison used in the present study it may be useful to review the major sources of variance with regard to death rates.

*Factors related to Death Rates*

1. *Age.* The age of the population at risk is very important. For example, death rates per 1,000 ranged from 0·64 at 20–24 years to 41·75 at 65–69 years among married men in 1958 [calculated from the Registrar General's figures; the method is described in the APPENDIX]. Both age-groups are within the age-range of parents of children attending psychiatric clinics.

2. *Sex*. Sex, too, is very relevant. In the same year (1958) the death rate at age 50–54 years for married men was 9·13 compared with 5·11 for married women.

3. *Marital status* is associated with surprisingly large variations in death rate (*Registrar General's Statistical Review of England and Wales for the two years 1946–7*, Text, Vol. I, Medical, H.M.S.O., 1951). In 1947 the ratio of the death rate for single women to that for married women was greater at all ages, with a peak of 66 per cent. excess at 30–34 years. Since 1930 the mortality of married women has sharply declined, whereas the mortality of single women has not fallen to the same extent. Consequently the mortality ratio of single women to married women has risen sharply and has continued to do so since 1947 (*Registrar General's Life Tables for 1951–2*). Among men, there was a similar ratio, single men having a death rate 86 per cent. higher than married men in the age group 45–49 years. The possible reasons for this difference include factors of marital selection arising from physical incapacity. However, the rate for the widowed and divorced was also greater than for the married, although the difference was not as great as that between the married and single. The explanation is probably complex, but one consideration is that within five-year age-groups, the widowed were slightly older than the married, and this may have influenced the findings, though it is unlikely to be the sole factor. Controlling for marital status is particularly important in a consideration of deaths among parents of children attending psychiatric clinics, for they include a disproportionate number of single and divorced parents.

4. *Socio-economic Status*. Until recently, there has been a gradient, the death rate being the lowest in the Registrar General's Class I and highest in Class V. However, partly owing to a reclassification of some occupations for the 1951 census, the association of mortality with social class has become less clear-cut. Men living in Greater London show a gradient in mortality rate from a trough in Class II to a peak in Class V, Class I is intermediate between II and III (*Registrar General: Occupational Mortality*, H.M.S.O., 1958). There are variations according to sex and to place of residence but in general the situation is much as before with the mortality of Class II low and Class V high, and that for Classes I and IV rather more variable.[1]

5. *Secular trends*. One of the most important factors, and the one least often considered in controlling for relevant variables, is the era. During this century death rates have fallen steadily; the standardized mortality ratio was 201 in 1910; 134 in 1930; 100 in 1950–2; and 91 in 1959 (*The Registrar General's Statistical Review of England and Wales for the year 1959*, Part I, Tables, Medical: H.M.S.O. 1960). These differences are striking, but if the groups were chosen from roughly the same period in the last thirty years, they would not give rise to gross discrepancies. However, parents are young

---

[1] Changes since the 1961 census have not been considered as the data from the study all relate to an earlier period.

adults and here the differences are much greater. For example, among men aged 35–39 years, the rate per 1,000 was 8·62 in 1906–10, 4·57 in 1938 and 2·42 in 1959, and for women was 7·05, 3·59 and 1·78. In the age-groups 20–25 years, the fall has been greater still, from 2·25 in 1938 to 0·53 in 1959 (figures for women). Among men, too, there has been a marked fall, apart from a considerable temporary rise during World War II. Thus in the parental age-range, very small differences in the years from which the groups were chosen could produce important and sizeable distortions.

### Observed and Expected Deaths among the Parents of Maudsley Children

With these considerations in mind, it was decided that the only satisfactory comparison would be that of the observed death rate with the expected rate calculated from the Registrar General's figures. The calculation was made separately for each year during the child's lifetime, according to the parent's age, sex, and marital status in that year, so that relevant variables were controlled [the method is described in the APPENDIX]. Place of residence and occupational status could not be taken into account. The former is unlikely to have been important, as the death rate does not vary greatly throughout England and Wales, and the rate for Greater London (the area from which most of the patients were drawn) is less, rather than greater, than the national average (*Registrar General's Statistical Review of England and Wales for the year 1959*, Part I, Tables, Medical). The social class distribution for Maudsley children does not differ significantly from that for Greater London [TABLE 5.2] but differs from that for the country as a whole in having a greater proportion in Class II, where the mortality is lower. There is, therefore, no reason to suppose that the significance of an excess rate of parental deaths would be artificially exaggerated, although it might be slightly underestimated.

TABLE 5.2

SOCIAL CLASS DISTRIBUTION OF MAUDSLEY CHILDREN

| Social class | Maudsley group No. | % | Greater London % |
|---|---|---|---|
| I and II | 149 | (21·8) | (21·5) |
| III | 350 | (51·3) | (54·7) |
| IV | 89 | (13·0) | (10·7) |
| V | 95 | (13·9) | (13·1) |
| Total known | 683 | | |
| Not known | 56 | | |

The observed and expected rates of parental death for the Maudsley children are shown in TABLE 5.3. The observed number of deaths of *fathers and mothers* are both more than double the expected number. These differences reach a high degree of statistical significance.

The significantly high rate of parental deaths receives confirmation from

### TABLE 5.3
#### PARENTAL DEATHS

|  | Deaths | | Significance | |
|---|---|---|---|---|
|  | Observed | Expected | $\chi^2$ | $p$ |
| Total parental deaths | 88 | 34·6 | 71·9 | <0·001 |
| Paternal deaths | 52 | 20·3 | 47·9 | <0·001 |
| Maternal deaths | 36 | 14·3 | 31·4 | <0·001 |

the only available figures from direct studies of rates of bereavement in children. In the National Survey there has been a longitudinal study of legitimate children throughout the country born during one week in 1946 (Douglas and Blomfield, 1958). At $4\frac{1}{4}$ years the number of children who had lost one or more parents through death was calculated (Rowntree, 1955). Of the group of 4,854 children studied, 67 (1·46 per cent.) had been bereaved by that age, compared with 27 out of 642 legitimate Maudsley children (4·21 per cent.). The critical ratio for the difference between proportions was 7·43, which is highly significant. Unpublished figures from the National Survey give a proportion of bereaved children at ages after $4\frac{1}{4}$ years: 2·66 per cent. at $6\frac{1}{4}$ years, 3·65 per cent. at $8\frac{1}{2}$ years, and 4·75 per cent. at $10\frac{3}{4}$ years (Clow, 1961); all are well below the comparable Maudsley figures. The Survey figures refer only to deaths of the first parent (a second parent died in approximately 0·1 per cent. of the population) and there were a few children (about 0·3 per cent.) for whom the circumstances were not known. At all ages the paternal deaths exceeded the maternal deaths by between 50 per cent. and 100 per cent.

The only other longitudinal study giving comparable data is the study of Newcastle upon Tyne infants (Miller et al., 1960). Of the 847 children studied (illegitimate children were included), 27 (3·19 per cent.) had lost a parent before the child reached five years. The figure for the Maudsley children is 33 out of 704 (4·69 per cent.). The rate of bereavement among Maudsley children was still greater but the difference is less and the reasons for the marked difference between the rate for Newcastle children and National Survey children must be considered. The extra nine months would not account for more than a slight increase. In addition, the Newcastle study began with an unduly low proportion in social classes I and II which was greatly exaggerated by a disproportionate loss of children from these classes during the first five years (53 per cent. of Class I and 33 per cent. of Class II were lost from the survey). Consequently the marked excess of children in Classes IV and V at the outset increased during the investigation. The mortality in these classes is higher than in Class II (Registrar General: Occupational Mortality, H.M.S.O., 1958) and might account for some of the difference. On the other hand, the social class differences for mortality are relatively small. A more important cause of the higher bereavement rate in the Newcastle study might be a higher death rate in the region: the standardized mortality ratio for Tyneside was 122 compared with 97 for London (*Registrar General: Occupational Mortality*, H.M.S.O., 1958).

Whether or not the excess of parental deaths was an artifact, connected with referral of the child to a psychiatric clinic, was difficult to determine. As will be shown later, in most cases parental death preceded the onset of the child's symptoms by several years, so that the death itself cannot often have been an important factor in the child's referral to a clinic. Nevertheless, the absence from home of one parent (through death) might have been related, as might have other consequences of parental death, such as re-marriage of the surviving spouse. Again, as shown later, usually there was also a long gap between parental remarriage and either onset of symptoms or referral to hospital.

There was no reason to suppose that bereaved children were referred to hospital earlier or for lesser disorders, as the distribution of number of symptoms, number of fields of disturbance, and duration of symptoms was closely similar to those for non-bereaved children. The only pointer towards a referral bias was the greater proportion of bereaved children among Maudsley *'non-disturbed'* than among children attending Dental or Paediatric clinics, but the proportion was still below that among *'disturbed'* children and the numbers are too small to give much weight to differences in either direction.

### Relationship between Death, Physical Illness and Mental Disorder in the Parent

Parental death cannot be considered only in isolation for it is preceded and followed by many changes. Some of these will be considered in more detail later but the overlap with physical and mental illness may usefully be examined at this point.

Some deaths were sudden or occurred after a relatively short illness but a third (31 of 88) took place after at least a year's illness and a quarter of all cases of chronic parental (physical) illness ended in death. The inter-relationship between mental disorder and chronic physical illness has already been considered.

In addition, at least three (probably four) deaths were due to suicide and another two were a consequence of already existing parental mental disorder. A number of other parents (including a rather unstable man who drowned when drunk) also had exhibited marked psychiatric abnormalities. Three surviving spouses had a psychiatric illness (as defined) within six months of the bereavement. Several others had severe disorders which did not receive psychiatric treatment, and other spouses developed a mental illness after a longer delay. Whether this amount of overt mental disorder is usually associated with parental death is not known, although Hinton (1963) found that dying patients were commonly depressed and often anxious, and that this was especially marked among those with schoolchildren. It may be that the parental distress before dying and the grief of the surviving parent is sometimes as important to the child as the death itself.

## Discussion and Conclusions

Over twice as many children attending a psychiatric clinic had lost a parent through death as would be expected from comparable death rates in the general population. In spite of a widespread emphasis in the literature on the importance of parent-child relationships and the harmful consequences for the child when the relationship is broken, the author was unable to find any previous systematic study of rates of bereavement among children with psychiatric disorder. Nevertheless, the present results are in keeping with earlier studies that have noted the frequency with which children showing psychiatric disorder come from 'broken homes'. The break-up of the home will be considered later, but what has been already noted is that parental death is often associated with parental mental disorder and/or chronic physical illness and that the inter-relationships between these must be taken into account as each has been shown to be associated with disorder in the child. Contrary to Bowlby's views on the special importance of *maternal* deprivation and childhood grief (Bowlby, 1960 and 1961a and b), paternal death and maternal death were *equally* associated with psychiatric disorder in the child.

# CHAPTER VI

# CHARACTERISTICS OF CHILDREN WITH PARENTS HAVING PSYCHIATRIC OR PHYSICAL ILLNESS

## I. CHILDREN WITH PSYCHIATRICALLY ILL PARENTS

THE 'disturbed' group was split into the 137 children with a psychiatrically ill parent (the 'psychiatric' group) and the 592 children neither of whose parents had or had had a psychiatric illness as defined (the 'other' group), and the two groups were then compared.

*Age*

The ages of all the children were known and recorded as the age on the child's last birthday. All patients who attended the Children's Department for the first time in 1955 or 1959 were included. Normally, children over the age of 16 years are not seen in the Department, but, a few children of 17 years were seen, usually because the child had been under 17 years when put on the waiting list. The distribution of ages is shown in FIGURE 6.1 [also in TABLE 6.1 in the APPENDIX].

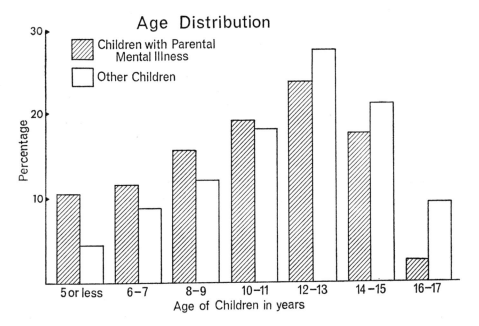

FIG. 6.1. Age distributions: Comparisons of child-patients with mentally ill parents and those without.

The mean and median ages of the groups differed to a highly significant extent (p<0·001), the *'psychiatric'* children being much younger. The age differences were consistent throughout, in that the proportion of *'psychiatric'* children was greater in all age groups under 12 years and less in all the higher age groups. But the greatest difference lay in the excess of *'psychiatric'* children in the under-five age group and the paucity among the 16- and 17-year-olds. The fact that children with mentally ill parents were generally younger than other children at the same clinic is particularly striking as the older children had the older parents, who might be expected to include more who had had a psychiatric illness.

## Sex and Social Class

The *'psychiatric'* and *'other'* groups showed the same sex distribution: approximately three boys to two girls. This male preponderance is usual in patients attending child psychiatric departments. There was no difference in social class (Registrar General's classification) between the two groups.

## Size of Sibship and Ordinal Position

No differences in size of sibship or position of the child-patient in his family were found between the *'psychiatric'* and *'other'* groups. In both [TABLE 6.2] there was a striking preponderance of children who were the eldest in their family, with a corresponding deficit of youngest children (of necessity, the two groups must normally be equal). This has been found by other workers (e.g. Goodenough and Leahy, 1927), although studies are sometimes contradictory (Spiegel and Bell, 1959). There was no distinction between children with and without parental mental illness.

### TABLE 6.2
### POSITION IN THE FAMILY OF CHILDREN

| Position in the family | Psychiatric No. | % | Other No. | % | Significance (critical ratio) |
|---|---|---|---|---|---|
| Eldest | 53 | (38·7) | 197 | (33·5) | N.S. |
| Youngest | 26 | (18·9) | 133 | (22·6) | N.S. |
| Only child | 25 | (18·3) | 115 | (19·6) | N.S. |
| Other position | 33 | (24·1) | 143 | (24·3) | N.S. |
| Total | 137 | | 588 | | |
| Not known | | | 4 | | |

## Separation from Parents

Separation from the mother, father, or both parents was defined as complete separation for one month or longer during the first five years of the child's life. It would have been preferable to compare the *'psychiatric'* and *'other'* groups with regard to separation for varying periods of time at different ages but the data were often inadequate for this, and it was decided to use only the one measure of separation. The period of one month was chosen because it was the period specified for the coding of data in the Department, and information was usually stated in the records in that form.

TABLE 6.3
SEPARATION FROM PARENTS

| Separation | Groups | | | | Significance | |
|---|---|---|---|---|---|---|
| | Psychiatric | | Other | | Critical ratio | p value |
| | No. | % | No. | % | | |
| From mother | 47 | (34·3) | 128 | (21·6) | 3·18 | <0·01 |
| From father | 57 | (41·6) | 183 | (30·9) | 2·38 | <0·02 |
| From both | 39 | (28·5) | 97 | (16·4) | 3·27 | <0·01 |
| Total | 137 | | 592 | | | |

Separation from one or both parents was significantly commoner among the children with mentally ill parents. In part this was because the parents' admission to hospital constituted an important cause of separation of the child from its parents. This often led to problems about care of the child, as Ekdahl and her colleagues (1962) found, but as will be shown later, some children were often less disturbed when away from the mentally ill parent than when with him or her.

*Anomalous Parenthood*

As pointed out in CHAPTER IV, many children attending psychiatric clinics and many delinquents have 'anomalous parents' or, as it is often stated, come from a 'broken home'. The frequency of 'broken homes' among clinic children is almost always greater than among normal children (usually the difference lies in the high rate among children with antisocial conduct disorders, the rate being lower among neurotic children (Banister and Ravden, 1944 and 1945; Wardle, 1961)). The homes have generally been 'broken' by separation or divorce (although deaths, too, have been important) and several writers have seen the connection between broken homes and childish conduct disorders as a reflection of the instability and psychiatric disorder in the parents which sometimes disrupts the marriage (Hirsch, 1937; Banister and Ravden, 1945). In view of this it seemed important to determine whether such a variable differentiated groups of children with and without psychiatrically ill parents. The term 'anomalous parent' has been preferred to that of 'broken home' as a more accurate description and was applied to any child who, at the time of first attending the Clinic, was living other than with his two natural parents. The term was not applied if one parent was temporarily absent through illness or other causes. The group was further broken down according to the reason for the situation—step-parent, death of parent, adoption, etc., (the categories were not mutually exclusive).

The proportion with anomalous parents was only slightly greater among the children with mentally ill parents than among the other children and

E

the difference did not reach statistical significance. Within the subgroups, however, step-parents and absent parents were both more common in the *'psychiatric'* group, and the latter difference was significant ($p<0.02$). It is particularly these forms of anomalous parenthood which other writers have thought to be most deleterious in their effects on children.

TABLE 6.4
ANOMALOUS PARENTHOOD

| | Groups | | | | Significance | |
|---|---|---|---|---|---|---|
| *Parent Situation* | *Psychiatric* | | *Other* | | *Critical ratio* | *p value* |
| | *No.* | *%* | *No.* | *%* | | |
| Total anomalous | 50 | *(36·5)* | 186 | *(31·4)* | N.S. | |
| Reason for anomaly | | | | | | |
| Foster parent or in care | 8 | *(5·8)* | 27 | *(4·6)* | N.S. | |
| Step-parent | 26 | *(19·0)* | 78 | *(13·2)* | N.S. | |
| Adoption | 1 | *(0·7)* | 27 | *(4·6)* | N.S. | |
| Parent absent | 15 | *(10·9)* | 32 | *(5·4)* | 2·39 | <0·02 |
| Parent dead | 13 | *(9·5)* | 72 | *(12·2)* | N.S. | |
| Total children | 137 | | 592 | | | |

Further comparisons were made to check whether among Maudsley children, as in other series, anomalous parenthood was an important variable relating to psychiatric disorder. The matched *'disturbed'* and *'non-disturbed'* groups [described above] are compared in TABLE 6.5.

TABLE 6.5
ANOMALOUS PARENTS IN DISTURBED AND NON-DISTURBED GROUPS

| | Groups | | | | Significance | |
|---|---|---|---|---|---|---|
| *Parent Situation* | *Disturbed* | | *Non-Disturbed* | | *Critical ratio* | *p* |
| | *No.* | *%* | *No.* | *%* | | |
| Total anomalous | 155 | *(29·1)* | 18 | *(18·0)* | 2·45 | <0·02 |
| Reason for anomaly | | | | | | |
| Foster parent or in care | 22 | | 3 | | | |
| Adoption | 21 | | 4 | | | |
| Step-parent | 69 | | 5 | | | |
| Parent absent | 35 | | 4 | | | |
| Parent dead | 51 | | 6 | | | |
| Total children | 532 | | 100 | | | |

More of the children with psychiatric disorder (29·1 per cent.) had anomalous parents than the children without disorder or with uncomplicated epilepsy, subnormality or organic disease (18 per cent.). This confirms that, among Maudsley children, as in other groups, anomalous parenthood is associated with child psychiatric disorder. There were similar differences between the Maudsley (22·8 per cent.) and Dental (6·2 per cent.) groups ($p<0.001$) and between the Maudsley (20·8 per cent.) and Paediatric (12·5 per cent.) groups. It should be noted that children with foster parents or 'in care' (one variety of anomalous parenthood) were expressly excluded from the last two comparisons. The figure for the Dental children may be unduly low, as the absence of a child's normal parent or parents might decrease the likelihood of his receiving Dental care.

## Intelligence

The intelligence of children who attended The Maudsley Hospital was routinely tested by psychologists, and in the great majority of cases the Wechsler Intelligence Scale for Children (WISC) was used. The Merrill Palmer Scale was used with the very young children for whom the WISC was inapplicable, and occasionally the Revised Stanford-Binet Scale or Matrices were used instead of the WISC. These tests have fairly high correlations with each other (Anastasi, 1954) and for the present purpose could be regarded as measuring much the same functions. The scores were made comparable by conversion to a mean of 100 with a standard deviation of 15 (for details of the procedure see Rutter, 1964).

The distribution of I.Q. scores for the *'psychiatric'* and *'other'* groups was closely similar and no difference reached significance [TABLE 6.6 in the APPENDIX]. Abnormalities of intelligence had been previously found to be of little importance in the aetiology of any child psychiatric disorder (Rutter, 1964).

## Diagnosis of the Child

There is no universally agreed classification of psychiatric disorder in childhood. The difficulties associated with classification according to different principles have been discussed by Kanner (1944) and Rutter (1963a). At present most diagnostic schemes use some variant of the antisocial conduct and neurotic dichotomy, which has to recommend it demonstrated differences in background factors (cf. Banister and Ravden, 1944 and 1945; Wardle, 1961), response to treatment (Cytryn et al., 1960), and long term prognosis (Morris et al., 1954; Morris et al., 1956). A study which utilized factor analysis delineated three groups; an 'unsocialized aggressive behaviour syndrome pattern', a 'socialized delinquency behaviour syndrome pattern', and an 'over-inhibited behaviour pattern' (Hewitt and Jenkins, 1946), which, in an independent study, were shown to differ with regard to various environmental variables (Lewis, 1954). This classification had to be rejected in the present study, as the traits used by Hewitt and Jenkins to delineate the syndromes (as, for example, 'inadequate guilt feelings', 'bad companions', 'seclusiveness') proved to be not readily applicable to the descriptions used in the Maudsley Children's Department.

O'Neal and Robins' 30-year follow-up study of children seen in a child guidance clinic used somewhat similar categories—'delinquency', 'aggressive or antisocial disorder' (applied only to children who had not yet experienced court action) and 'neurotic' disorder—categories shown to differ strikingly in their long-term prognosis (O'Neal and Robins, 1958, 1959; O'Neal *et al.*, 1960).

Because of the validity and ease of application of this classification a similar one was used for the present study. In addition to neurotic illness (N.I.)— (i.e. a syndrome which approximated to the adult form of neurosis; anxiety state, hysteria, obsessional state etc.), neurotic behaviour disorder (N.B.D.) aggressive or antisocial conduct behaviour disorder (C.B.D.) and delinquency, a further category of mixed behaviour disorder (M.B.D.) was used for an admixture of neurotic and antisocial symptoms in which neither predominated.[1]

TABLE 6.7

DIAGNOSIS OF CHILDREN

*Diagnosis of Child*

| Group | N.I. | | N.B.D. | | M.B.D. | | C.B.D. | | Delinquency | | Total |
|---|---|---|---|---|---|---|---|---|---|---|---|
| | No. | % | No. | % | No. | % | No. | % | No. | % | |
| Psychiatric | 21 | (17·4) | 43 | (17·2) | 24 | (28·2) | 29 | (18·7) | 20 | (15·6) | 137 |
| Other | 99 | | 204 | | 58 | | 125 | | 106 | | 592 |
| Total | 120 | | 247 | | 82 | | 154 | | 126 | | 729 |

The diagnoses of the '*psychiatric*' and '*other*' group children are given in TABLE 6.7, the percentages are the proportion of each diagnostic group whose parents were mentally ill. More children in the mixed behaviour disorder group had parents with psychiatric disorder than in any other diagnostic group. The proportion diagnosed mixed behaviour disorder is 28·2 per cent. in the '*psychiatric*' group and 18·5 per cent. in the '*other*' group; the difference being significant ($p < 0.02$). However, this diagnosis was made only when the child could not be fitted into any other category and might well be made if the child exhibited a large number of symptoms. Comparison of the diagnostic groups according to number of symptoms and fields of disturbance showed that children with a mixed behaviour disorder had more severe ($p < 0.001$) and more widespread ($p < 0.001$) disorders. Thus, the excess of mixed behaviour disorders in the '*psychiatric*' group was a reflection of the already demonstrated tendency of these children to have more severe disorders.

*Fields of Disturbance and Symptoms of the 'Psychiatric' and 'Other' Children*

Comparison of the '*psychiatric*' and '*other*' groups is shown in TABLES 6.8 to 6.16 in the APPENDIX.

For no symptoms was the frequency in the '*other*' group significantly greater than in the '*psychiatric*' group. The following symptoms occurred significantly more frequently in the group whose parents were mentally ill: anxiety, disobedience, aggression or temper tantrums, disturbed relationship with the mother and sibs, hyperactivity, gratification and tension habits, and disorders of sleeping. These are not such as to create a coherent picture of

[1] Definitions are included in the APPENDIX.

the disturbance particularly associated with parental psychiatric illness but certain conclusions may be drawn.

Delinquent symptoms were conspicuously absent from the symptoms occurring with greater frequency among the 'psychiatric' children. This suggests that delinquency is not especially associated with mental illness in the parent. Rather more surprisingly, psychic symptoms (other than anxiety) were also no more frequent in the offspring of mentally ill parents. Perhaps this is in keeping with the findings of O'Neal and Robins (O'Neal et al., 1960) that most neurotic children did *not* become neurotic adults, indeed only a few more became neurotic adults than those in their group who had been 'normal' as children.

The more frequent symptoms might be thought to reflect disordered relationships within the family; manifest disturbance in relationship to parents and sibs, disobedience, aggression and temper tantrums. Bethell (1958) related tension habits to restriction of the child and to depression in either parent, and Sharma (1950) considered that gratification habits were associated with lack of emotional warmth in the parents (this must be regarded as not proven, as he did not use a control group). Consequently, it might be said that the symptoms were those particularly associated with lack of harmony between parent and child, often a feature of parental psychiatric illness. However, as so little is known about the symptoms of childhood disorder not much store can be set, at present, on the associations of particular symptoms with parental illness.

*Attendance at the Clinic, and Outcome of Treatment*

Much has been written about the influence of parental attitudes on regularity of attendance at the clinic, and on outcome of treatment (see, for example, Witmer, 1933). The effect of parental expectations of the role they are to play in treatment has also been studied (e.g. Maas, 1955). As previous psychiatric treatment of the parent might influence these variables, the 'psychiatric' and 'other' groups were compared with regard to attendance and outcome.

When children are first seen at The Maudsley Hospital they are considered at a conference attended by the people chiefly concerned with their treatment: the psychiatrist, psychologist, and psychiatric social worker. Whether the child requires or will benefit from treatment is decided at that time. More children in the 'psychiatric' group were accepted for treatment (88·1 per cent.) than among the remainder (71·5 per cent.), and the difference was significant (p<0·01). This might have been solely because of their more severe disorders or because a parent who was ill increased the likelihood that the child would be accepted for treatment, but unfortunately, the number was too small to control for severity of disorder.

Many children first seen in 1959 were still attending at the time of this study, so comparisons regarding treatment and outcome were restricted to the 1955 group. No significant differences between the *'psychiatric'* and *'other'* groups were found for duration of attendance, number of attendances, proportion treated as in-patients, regularity of attendance (measured by proportion who 'lapsed' or failed appointments), or outcome, but fewer (18·8 per cent.) of the children with psychiatrically ill parents were categorized as 'recovered' or 'much improved' (as against 35·8 per cent. in the *'other'* group). This difference fell only just short of the 5 per cent. level of significance.

*Placement*

Recommendations of various kinds were often made regarding placement. For this study, those in which removal of the child from home was advised were grouped under the term 'residential placement' (which included any type of residential school, approved school, foster home or 'in care', or any recommendation for removal from the parents, other than admission to hospital). Of the 59 children with mentally ill parents 27·0 per cent. were placed away from home, some three times higher than the proportion in the *'other'* group (9·6 per cent.); the difference is highly significant ($p < 0.001$). However, severity [TABLE 6.17] and extent of disorder are both highly related to the frequency with which residential placement was advised ($p < 0.001$ in both cases). Many more severely ill children were placed away from home.

TABLE 6.17

RELATIONSHIP BETWEEN SEVERITY OF DISORDER AND
RESIDENTAL PLACEMENT

| | Number of symptoms | | | | | | |
|---|---|---|---|---|---|---|---|
| | *1–6* | | *7–9* | | *10 or more* | | *Total* |
| | *No. of children* | % | *No. of children* | % | *No. of children* | % | *No. of children* |
| Residential placement | 9 | *(6·0)* | 12 | *(12·2)* | 20 | *(32·3)* | 41 |
| No residential placement | 140 | | 86 | | 42 | | 268 |
| Total | 149 | | 98 | | 62 | | 309 |

Chi-square $= 26·308$    2 d.f.    $p < 0.001$

The *'psychiatric'* and *'other'* groups were again compared, with the severity and extent of disorder equated in the two groups [FIGURE 6.2]. Even when severity and extent of the disorder were held constant, residential placement was more commonly advised for children with mentally ill parents. The difference was significant only for the most severe disorder group but the numbers were small and comparable differences for disorders of moderate and wide extent fell only just short of the 5 per cent. level of significance. The differences were not present, however, in the mild and circumscribed disorders.

During 1955 and 1959 there was no particular policy in the Department with regard to the treatment or placement of children whose parents had a mental illness and there was no evidence that the difference in the number removed from home was merely a reflection of preconceived ideas among the psychiatrists in charge. In fact, it was evident, when the records were examined, that residential placement had sometimes been made only with reluctance, after it had become abundantly clear that the child's disorder was being seriously aggravated by remaining at home. Often this relationship was underlined when the child improved on removal from home and relapsed on return. When this occurred the symptoms of the parent frequently directly involved the child in some way [see CHAPTER VIII]. The greater proportion of 'psychiatric' children removed from home might have been due to the fact that influence of a mentally ill parent was more harmful or less subject to change than when the parent was not ill, but this cannot be definitely concluded from the available data.

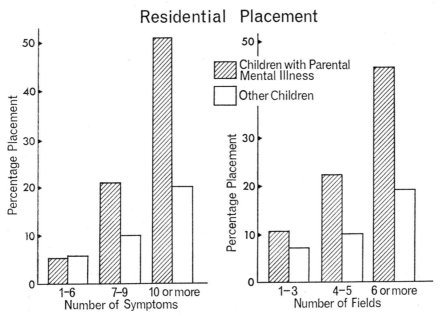

FIG. 6.2. Child-patients recommended for residential placement: Comparison of those with mentally ill parent and those without
(a) with the number of symptoms held constant
(b) with the number of fields of disturbance held constant.

*Psychiatric Disorder in the Sibs*

When considering the effects of parental mental illness on the children, it is important to know whether the influence is confined to one child or whether other children in the family are also adversely affected. For this reason the proportion of children with psychiatrically disturbed sibs was compared between the 'psychiatric' and 'other' groups. Generally, the disorders in the sibs were not described in sufficient detail for diagnostic assessment to have much meaning. Therefore, disorders were divided into three groups: (*a*) sibs who had been referred to a psychiatrist, (*b*) sibs who had been before a court for any offence committed by them, and (*c*) sibs who fell into neither of the first two groups but for whom there was good evidence of a neurotic or conduct disorder severe enough to require psychiatric treatment. Temper tantrums, 'difficult behaviour' or anxiety were not in themselves sufficient to include a child in this category.

TABLE 6.18
PSYCHIATRIC DISORDER IN SIBS

| Number of Children having:— | Groups | | | Significance | |
| | Psychiatric | Other | | Critical ratio | *p* |
| | No. % | No. % | | | |
| Sibs treated by psychiatrist | 20 (*14·6*) | 31 | (*5·2*) | 3·917 | 0·0001 |
| Delinquent sibs | 8 (*5·8*) | 26 | (*4·4*) | N.S. | |
| Sibs having other psychiatric disorder | 17 (*12·4*) | 39 | (*6·6*) | 2·32 | <0·03 |
| Total: sibs with any psychiatric disorders | 44 (*32·2*) | 84 | (*14·2*) | 5·0 | <0·0001 |
| Total children | 137 | 592 | | | |

A third of the '*psychiatric*' children had sibs who also had a psychiatric disorder, compared with only one in seven of the children in the '*other*' group. This difference is very highly significant ($p < 0.0001$). Moreover, the proportion (14·2 per cent.) in the '*other*' group (all '*disturbed*' children) was itself twice that in the '*non-disturbed*' group (7·5 per cent.); the difference is probably significant ($p < 0.04$). The differences between the '*psychiatric*' and '*other*' groups were confined, however, to sibs treated by a psychiatrist and to sibs with untreated disorders. Delinquent children were found equally in the two groups. This supports the conclusion, drawn earlier, that delinquency is *not* particularly related to parental psychiatric disorder.

The number of sibs with psychiatric disorder (as defined) is obviously a minimum figure in that others had less severe disorders and yet others were still young and might develop psychiatric illness later in childhood. Even so, the causal factors of disorder in children with mentally ill parents were often not confined to the patient, but adversely influenced many of the children in the family. This was so to a greater extent than with the disorders of other children at the same clinic.

## II. CHILDREN WITH PHYSICALLY ILL PARENTS

Children whose parents had a physical disorder were next compared in the same way.

### Age

The distribution of ages [see TABLE 6.19 in the APPENDIX] did not differ in the children whose parents had a recurrent illness (the *'recurrent'* group), had a chronic illness (the *'chronic'* group) or who had no illness or only an acute illness (the *'other'* group). There was not an excess of older children, although an excess had been expected because of the increased chance for the older children to have a physically ill parent (owing to the greater number of years at risk and to the higher proportion of older parents). This suggests that a *relatively* greater number of *younger* children had physically ill parents. Unfortunately, this could not be checked.

### Sex and Social Class

The proportion of boys and girls was similar in the three groups and there were no significant differences in social class distribution [TABLE 6.20 in the APPENDIX]. However, probably reflecting a similar trend in the general population, there was a non-significant tendency for children with parents who were ill to come from classes IV and V (the semi-skilled and unskilled occupations).

### Diagnosis of the Child and Referral Agency

The distribution of diagnostic categories was fairly similar (TABLE 6.21), and a chi-square performed on the five by three table was not statistically significant. In line with previous studies, however, the proportion of delinquents was higher in the *'recurrent'* (23·2 per cent.) and *'chronic'* (22·1 per cent.) groups than in the *'other'* (15·5 per cent.). When *'recurrent'* and *'chronic'* were combined and compared with the *'other'* the difference was significant ($p < 0.02$). This was also reflected in a similar excess of *'recurrent'* and *'chronic'* children referred by the probation service, remand homes, or courts (20·0 per cent. and 21·1 per cent. respectively) compared with 13·5 per cent. among the *'other'* children.

TABLE 6.21
DIAGNOSIS OF CHILD

| Diagnosis | Groups | | |
| | Recurrent No. % | Chronic No. % | Other No. % |
| --- | --- | --- | --- |
| Neurotic illness | 13 (*13·7*) | 18 (*18·9*) | 90 (*16·4*) |
| Neurotic behaviour disorder | 31 (*32·5*) | 25 (*26·3*) | 194 (*35·3*) |
| Mixed behaviour disorder | 9 (*9·5*) | 11 (*11·6*) | 65 (*11·8*) |
| Conduct behaviour disorder | 20 (*21·1*) | 20 (*21·1*) | 115 (*20·9*) |
| Delinquency | 22 (*23·2*) | 21 (*22·1*) | 85 (*15·5*) |
| Total | 95 | 95 | 549 |

The differences, although significant, were small and the overall distribution of diagnoses was very similar in the three groups. The excess of delinquents among children whose parents had a recurrent or chronic physical illness may have been a function of referral bias, as suggested by the absence of any difference in the proportion of children with non-delinquent disorders of conduct. The main difference between the delinquent and non-delinquent children with antisocial conduct disorders was that the former had been taken to court whereas the latter had not. However, the non-delinquent group also contained a number of disobedient, destructive, aggressive children who had not committed any offence.

### Anomalous Parenthood and Separation from Parents

The overall rate of anomalous parenthood showed no significant difference between the 'chronic', 'recurrent' and 'other' groups but, as already mentioned, there was a significant excess of bereaved children in the 'chronic' group (23·2 per cent. as against 9·5 per cent. in the 'recurrent' and 'other' groups). Because of parents' admission to hospital or death rather more of the 'chronic' and 'recurrent' children had also been separated from their parents for a month or more in the first five years of life.

### Other Factors

As already shown, duration of symptoms and severity and extent of disorder of the children in the 'recurrent' and 'chronic' groups did not differ from the remainder of the children attending The Maudsley Hospital.

### Discussion and Conclusions

Children with mentally ill parents differed from other children attending the same clinic only in a few ways. More boys than girls developed neurotic or antisocial disorders. The reason for the sex difference is not known and possibly factors of referral play a part, but in studies of unselected schoolchildren it has usually been found that more boys than girls are 'maladjusted' or have some psychiatric or behavioural disorder (Cummings, 1944; Ullman, 1952). Enuresis is commoner in boys (Blomfield and Douglas, 1956; Lapouse and Monk, 1958); on the other hand, fears may be commoner in girls (Cummings, 1944; Lapouse and Monk, 1959). Girls may have greater opportunities than boys for inter-action with the parent of their own sex and this may exert a protective effect (Weinstein and Geisel, 1960). Why the sex distribution should be the reverse of that found among mentally ill adults requires investigation. One reason may be that whereas much of delinquency is regarded as a psychiatric problem, very little adult criminality is. Whatever the explanation, the sex differential did not distinguish the children of mentally ill parents from others at the same clinic.

Break-up of the home and separation from one or both parents had frequently occurred among the children whose parents were ill. These may have been important factors in the development of disorder in some of the children, and the deleterious effect of parental illness may partly have operated through this mechanism. Certainly, within the clinic population children who were not living with their two natural parents were more likely to have a psychiatric disorder. On the other hand, although parental *absence* may sometimes have been harmful, the *presence* of a mentally ill parent in the home was also harmful [cf. CHAPTER VIII].

Whatever the causal factors associated with parental mental illness, they were often not restricted to the patient, in that twice as many children (compared with others attending the same clinic) had sibs who also exhibited psychiatric disorder. Among children whose parents were mentally ill it was common for several to be affected, but when the parents were well, usually only one child in the family showed disorder. When a parent had psychiatric disorder, either the susceptibility of more of the children was greater, or the aetiological factors had a general effect on the offspring rather than a specific effect on one child.

Neither physical nor mental illness in the parent was associated with a specific behaviour syndrome in the children, but a considerable proportion of aggressive, anxious and disobedient younger children who had disturbed relationships with the rest of the family was found among the offspring of mentally ill parents. There was no particular association with delinquency and surprisingly few children had neurotic symptoms other than anxiety. In contrast, the children of physically ill parents were more often delinquent, although this may have been in part due to referral biases. They were not as young as the children with mentally ill parents but probably there was a relative paucity of older children. With both varieties of parental illness the younger child may be most at risk. Whether this is because the younger children have more contact with their parents and the contact with a parent who is ill is harmful, whether deleterious circumstances have more effect on the more immature organism, or whether other factors are more important remains uncertain.

The existence of parents who themselves had been under psychiatric care seemed to make little difference to the child's response to treatment. Just as many children failed appointments or stopped attending, appointments were as frequent and attendance lasted the same time. The outcome when the case was closed was much the same except that fewer of the children with mentally ill parents tended to do really well. The one striking difference was that a much higher proportion of children with parents who had a psychiatric disorder were placed in a residential school or elsewhere than in the care of their own parents. As far as could be determined this was not because the doctors in charge considered that children should not remain with mentally ill parents. The decision was usually forced by the child's deterioration at home and his improvement when away. This suggests an intimate interaction between the mentally ill child and the mentally ill parent which will be considered in more detail later.

# CHAPTER VII

# BEREAVED CHILDREN

AN ASSOCIATION between the death of either parent and psychiatric disorder in the children says nothing about the relationship between the two. The child's disorder might be a morbid grief reaction, or a reaction to circumstances in the home consequent upon parental death or to the situation associated with the illness that led to the death, or the death might merely be the event precipitating referral to the clinic; and, of course, other possibilities exist. Examination of the characteristics of the bereaved children and of the temporal aspects of the relationship may throw light on the nature of the interaction between parental death and disorder in the child.

## The Age of the Child at the Time of Bereavement

A significantly high rate of death among both fathers and mothers of children attending The Maudsley Hospital has been shown, but is this excess of deaths restricted to a particular period in the child's life? Unfortunately, figures for parental deaths at different ages of children in the general population were not available for comparison, but an indirect assessment was made. TABLE 7.1 shows parental deaths as they occur, according to two-year age periods during the life of the children, and FIGURE 7.1 shows the cumulative rate of bereavement at different ages.

TABLE 7.1

PARENTAL DEATHS BY AGE OF CHILD AT PARENTAL DEATH
(WAR DEATHS EXCLUDED)

| Age of child (years) | No. of parental deaths | No. of children | Children bereaved % | Corrected % | Cumulative % |
|---|---|---|---|---|---|
| Not born | 1 | 734 | 0·14 | 0·14 | 0·14 |
| 0–1 | 7 | 734 | 0·95 | 0·95 | 1·09 |
| 2–3 | 20 | 724 | 2·76 | 2·44 | 3·85 |
| 4–5 | 15 | 705 | 2·13 | 1·99 | 5·98 |
| 6–7 | 10 | 661 | 1·51 | 1·19 | 7·49 |
| 8–9 | 10 | 579 | 1·73 | 0·84 | 9·22 |
| 10–11 | 9 | 465 | 1·94 | 0·79 | 11·16 |
| 12–13 | 7 | 300 | 2·33 | 0·77 | 13·49 |
| 14–15 | 3 | 128 | 2·34 | 0·61 | 15·83 |
| 16–17 | 3 | 29 | 10·34 | 2·57 | 26·17 |
| Total | 85 | 734 | — | — | — |

Apart from a high rate at 16–17 years based on a very small number of cases, the greatest proportion of deaths occurred in the third and fourth years of the child's life. The age periods are not strictly comparable, in that the parents of the older children were themselves older and thereby subject to a higher expected death rate. It was not possible to correct for this entirely, but the comparability of different age periods was improved by correcting for the mean age of parents at the different ages of the children [TABLE 7.2].

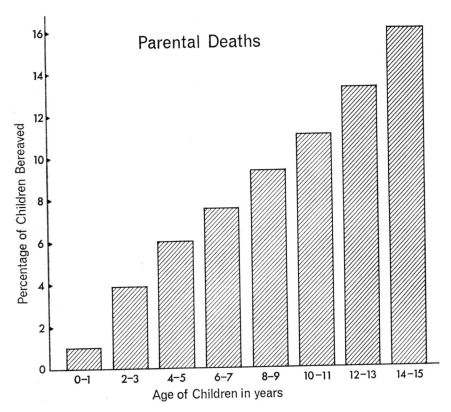

FIG. 7.1. Proportion of child-patients with a deceased parent according to the age of the children.

TABLE 7.2
DEATH RATES OF PARENTS ACCORDING TO AGE OF CHILD

| Age of children (years) | Mean age of father (years) | Death rate (per 1000) | Mean age of mother (years) | Death rate (per 1000) | Death rate parents for age of child (per 1000) |
|---|---|---|---|---|---|
| 2–3 | 33·13 | 1·25 | 31·38 | 0·95 | 1·13 |
| 4–5 | 32·3 | 1·20 | 30·55 | 0·88 | 1·07 |
| 6–7 | 33·75 | 1·30 | 34·65 | 1·20 | 1·26 |
| 8–9 | 40·21 | 2·25 | 39·07 | 1·75 | 2·05 |
| 10–11 | 42·59 | 2·90 | 39·86 | 1·80 | 2·46 |
| 12–13 | 44·65 | 3·60 | 41·80 | 2·13 | 3·01 |
| 14–15 | 47·07 | 4·75 | 43·04 | 2·40 | 3·81 |
| 16–17 | 47·27 | 5·0 | 44·71 | 2·55 | 4·02 |

The death rates for married men and women are shown separately for the different mean ages of parent, and the last column shows the calculated death rate for parents for each age of child (the ratio of paternal to maternal deaths was taken into consideration). The proportion of children bereaved in each age period was then divided by this figure, and a corrected proportion obtained [column 5 of TABLE 7.1]. After correction, the excess of parental deaths in the third and fourth years of life was even more marked: the corrected figures for two to five years are more than double those for any other age period up to 16 years. Several important variables need to be equated before different age-periods can be compared reliably, and this could be done only in part, so conclusions must be drawn with caution. Nevertheless, the parental death rate in these early years is so much higher than in later years (or in the first two years) that the findings provide some evidence that these years constitute a critical period in the child's development.

Comparable statistics for the general population are not available, but the National Survey figures offer some confirmation. The bereavement figure for $4\frac{1}{4}$ years has already been given and there was no breakdown according to age for younger children. Between $4\frac{1}{4}$ and $6\frac{1}{4}$ years a further 0·9 per cent. were bereaved, between $6\frac{1}{4}$ and $8\frac{1}{2}$ years 0·99 per cent. and in the next $2\frac{1}{4}$ years 1·10 per cent. (Clow, 1961). The age-periods for Maudsley children were not quite the same, but between four and six years 2·13 per cent. were bereaved, between six and eight years 1·51 per cent., and in the next two years 1·73 per cent. Thus the difference in bereavement rate is most marked in the younger child. As the ages were not exactly comparable and as there were no figures for the separate years before $4\frac{1}{4}$ years, all that can be said is that the National Survey figures are consistent with the hypothesis that the excess was most marked in the third and fourth years and that these years have a relatively greater importance for the child with regard to bereavement.

The death rates for mothers and for fathers were raised to approximately

TABLE 7.3

AGE OF CHILD AT DEATH OF FATHER AND MOTHER COMPARED

| Age (in years) | No. of children in age group at death of father | No. of children in age group at death of mother |
|---|---|---|
| Not born | 2 | — |
| 0–1 | 8 | 2 |
| 2–3 | 9 | 11 |
| 4–5 | 9 | 6 |
| 6–7 | 6 | 4 |
| 8–9 | 8 | 3 |
| 10–11 | 7 | 2 |
| 12–13 | 4 | 3 |
| 14–15 | 1 | 2 |
| 16–17 | — | 3 |
| Total | 54 | 36 |

the same extent. There was nothing to suggest that psychiatric disorder was related more to the death of the mother than to that of the father, or vice versa. It remains to be seen whether maternal or paternal deaths were more important at any particular age-period. The deaths of each parent at different ages of children are compared in TABLE 7.3.

The deaths in the two to three year age period tended slightly to be particularly those of mothers, but the numbers for each age period were too small for meaningful comparison. To compare larger groups the children were divided into those above and those below the age of $4\frac{1}{4}$ years at the time of parental death [TABLE 7.4].

TABLE 7.4

SEX OF DEAD PARENT ACCORDING TO AGE OF CHILD

| Parent dead | Age of Child | | | |
|---|---|---|---|---|
| | Less than $4\frac{1}{4}$ years | | More than $4\frac{1}{4}$ years | |
| | No. | % | No. | % |
| Father | 21 | (58·3) | 29 | (58·0) |
| Mother | 14 | (38·9) | 18 | (36·0) |
| Both | 1 | (2·8) | 3 | (6·0) |
| Total | 36 | | 50 | |

Chi-square not significant

The proportions of paternal and maternal deaths were closely similar for both age-groups. It seems that the deaths of mothers and fathers had a similar relative influence throughout childhood.

*Temporal Relationship between Parental Death and Psychiatric Disorder in the Child*

The timing of the onset of the child's symptoms and of his first attendance at hospital in relation to the death of his parent are shown in TABLE 7.5 and graphically in FIGURE 7.2.

TABLE 7.5

PERIOD OF TIME BETWEEN BEREAVEMENT AND DISORDER OF CHILD

| Period | No. of children having such a duration before onset of symptoms | No. of children having such a duration before attendance at hospital |
|---|---|---|
| Not known | 17 | — |
| 5 years or more | 25 | 56 |
| 4 years but less than 5 | 5 | 6 |
| 3 years but less than 4 | 5 | 6 |
| 2 years but less than 3 | 2 | 5 |
| 1 year but less than 2 | 2 | 2 |
| 7 months but less than 1 year | 3 | 6 |
| 6 months or less | 14 | 5 |
| Parental death occurring afterwards | 13 | — |
| Total children | 86 | 86 |

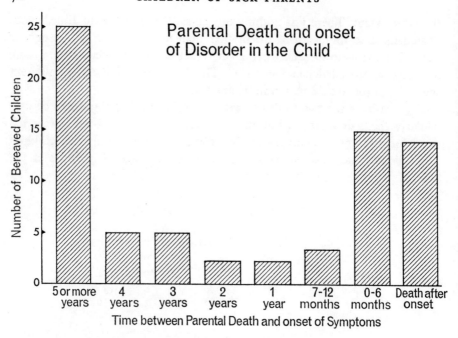

F<small>IG</small>. 7.2. The temporal relationship between parental death and onset of disorder in the child-patient.

In only a few children did the illness follow closely upon the bereavement and in nearly a *third* of the children there was a gap of five years or more. In about a sixth of cases the parental death did not occur until after the child first developed symptoms. In these the death may have been related only to referral to hospital, but may also have been relevant to the child's disorder,

TABLE 7.6

CHILDREN WITH ONSET OF SYMPTOMS WITHIN
6 MONTHS OF BEREAVEMENT

| Sex | Age | Diagnosis |
|---|---|---|
| Male | 15 years | Anxiety-depression |
| Male | 11 years | Depressive illness |
| Male | 14 years | Depressive illness |
| Male | 6 years | Depressive illness |
| Male | 12 years | Neurotic behaviour disorder (with marked anxiety and depression) |
| Female | 3 years | Neurotic behaviour disorder |
| Male | 13 years | Mixed behaviour disorder |
| Male | 14 years | Conduct disorder |
| Male | 15 years | Conduct disorder |
| Male | 12 years | Conduct disorder |
| Male | 11 years | Conduct disorder |
| Male | 8 years | Conduct disorder |
| Female | 8 years | Conduct disorder |
| Female | 14 years | Conduct disorder |

in that the child may have reacted adversely to circumstances associated with the parent's terminal illness. In 14 children symptoms first developed within six months of bereavement. Although these form a minority of bereaved children the number is greater than for any other single six-month period. The group was too small for further breakdown, but the 14 were somewhat atypical in their clinical picture.

Most were adolescent boys with either a depressive illness (in which features associated with adult grief reactions were sometimes prominent) or disorders of conduct. There were few young children and only two with neurotic behaviour disorders. Thus, immediate morbid reactions to bereavement were found chiefly in adolescents and were mainly shown by depression or antisocial behaviour. As there were so few children of this kind the findings can be regarded only as suggestive.

What can be said is that in most cases the child's disorder was not manifest until long after the parent's death and it seemed probable that factors consequent upon the death were more important than the death itself. These factors were many and various. The relationship between death and illness, physical and mental, has already been considered, as has the association with psychiatric disorder in the surviving spouse. Parental death often caused profound changes in the family. Children were often subject to a variety of upheavals, were looked after by several different relatives and friends, and eight were completely removed from their homes soon after the death of their parents. Somewhat less than half the parents (36) subsequently remarried. As important readjustments might be required of the child at such a time the temporal relationship between remarriage and onset of disorder in the child was examined [TABLE 7.7]. As with death, in only a few cases did parental remarriage have a close temporal relationship with the child's illness. If bereavement was a causal factor, its influence was usually indirect and delayed, no one event having a consistently close connection with the timing of the child's illness.

TABLE 7.7
PERIOD OF TIME BETWEEN PARENTAL REMARRIAGE
AND DISORDER OF CHILD

| Period | No. of children having such a duration before onset of symptoms | No. of children having such a duration before attendance at hospital |
|---|---|---|
| Not known | 9 | 5 |
| 5 years or more | 9 | 17 |
| 4 years but less than 5 | 2 | 3 |
| 3 years but less than 4 | 3 | 3 |
| 2 years but less than 3 | 2 | — |
| 1 year but less than 2 | — | 5 |
| 7 months but less than 1 year | — | 2 |
| 6 months or less | 5 | 1 |
| Remarriage occurring afterwards | 6 | — |

F

*Age and Sex*

The sex distribution of the bereaved children did not differ significantly from that of other children attending The Maudsley Hospital.

Bereaved children were markedly older than other children attending The Maudsley Hospital. This was to be expected, in that the older the child the more likely he is to have lost a parent. Consideration of the age distribution of the whole group of bereaved children is therefore without much meaning. For this reason, only those children bereaved before the age of 4¼ years were compared with other Maudsley children [TABLE 7.8]. The number of children involved was small but when the groups were compared according to the proportion above and below the age of 12, 69·4 per cent. of bereaved children were in the older age group compared with only 53·4 per cent. of the *'other'* children; the difference fell just short of significance (p<0·07). This is consistent with the previous finding that usually a long time elapses between parental death and development of disorder in the child; children bereaved in infancy frequently did not develop psychiatric disorder until adolescence.

TABLE 7.8
AGE OF CHILD

| Age of child (years) | Children bereaved before aged 4¼ years | | Children Other children | |
|---|---|---|---|---|
| | No. | % | No. | % |
| 5 or less | 1 | (2·8) | 37 | (5·2) |
| 6–7 | 2 | (5·6) | 68 | (9·7) |
| 8–9 | 4 | (11·1) | 91 | (12·9) |
| 10–11 | 4 | (11·1) | 131 | (18·6) |
| 12–13 | 13 | (36·1) | 181 | (25·7) |
| 14–15 | 9 | (25·0) | 140 | (19·9) |
| 16–17 | 3 | (8·3) | 55 | (7·8) |
| Total | 36 | | 703 | |

*Diagnosis*

To a lesser extent than with those children who became ill within six months of bereavement, there was an excess of neurotic illness and delinquency among the bereaved children [TABLE 7.9]. Both differences fell far short of significance but the deficiency of children with neurotic behaviour disorders was significant (p<0·01). This is due, at least in large part, to the age difference between the *'bereaved'* and *'other'* children.

*Discussions and Conclusions*

All investigators have found that many perfectly healthy adults were bereaved during childhood, so that in only a few cases is the outcome unfavourable. Moreover, when bereavement is followed by pathological

TABLE 7.9
DIAGNOSIS OF CHILD

| Diagnosis | Children Bereaved children | | Other children | | Significance Critical ratio | p |
|---|---|---|---|---|---|---|
| | No. | % | No. | % | | |
| N.I. | 20 | *(23·3)* | 101 | *(15·5)* | 0·927 | *0·4* |
| N.B.D. | 18 | *(20·9)* | 232 | *(35·5)* | 2·755 | *0·01* |
| M.B.D. | 12 | *(13·9)* | 73 | *(11·2)* | N.S. | |
| C.B.D. | 17 | *(19·8)* | 138 | *(21·1)* | N.S. | |
| Delinquency | 19 | *(22·1)* | 109 | *(16·7)* | 1·255 | *0·3* |
| Total | 86 | | 653 | | | |

development its course is far from uniform. The childhood disorders associated with parental loss in the present study were heterogeneous, but apart from child psychiatric disorder, parental death in childhood has been connected with adult neurosis and psychopathy (Gregory, 1958; Norton, 1952; Oswald, 1958; Barry and Lindemann, 1960; Earle and Earle, 1961), depression (Brown, 1961), attempted suicide (Greer, 1964), and possibly (although the findings were more contradictory) schizophrenia (Barry, 1949; Barry and Bousfield, 1937; Gerard and Siegel, 1950; Rosenzweig and Bray, 1943; Wahl, 1954 and 1956). In most studies the excess of parental deaths was largely restricted to early childhood and the few negative studies in the literature either lumped together all parental deaths occurring before adulthood (e.g. Ingham, 1949; Oltman et al., 1952) or regarded the differences as unimportant (Petursson, 1961). Few of the studies were satisfactory and the types of error have been categorized by Gregory (1958). Nevertheless, although many studies were poorly controlled, the better investigations have confirmed an association between parental death during early childhood and adult psychiatric disorder, at least as regards psychoneurosis and psychopathy. Recent bereavement has been shown to be associated with depression (Parkes, 1964) and on less evidence other writers have regarded it as a causal or precipitating factor in a wide range of physical and mental ailments (Parkes, 1964). Although bereavement in childhood is related to the development of child psychiatric disorder it certainly does not give rise to any specific abnormality.

The association was most marked in children aged two to five years, a period, perhaps, slightly later than that postulated by Bowlby (1961a) but in keeping with the general view that the younger child is more susceptible. It is not strictly a 'critical period', in that the child is also vulnerable (although less so) at other ages. Recent evidence, however, suggests that the 'critical periods' noted by ethologists (particularly in birds) also are not as clearly delimited as once thought (Hinde et al., 1956; Moltz, 1960). This is not to say that the pre-school child was more likely to develop an immediate morbid grief reaction, though it should be noted that reactions to hospital admission have been found to be most marked in the pre-school child (Prugh et al.,

1953; Schaffer and Callender, 1959). Psychiatric disturbance following parental death was usually delayed many years, often until early adolescence and only a minority of the children developed symptoms soon after their parent died. They were mainly adolescents with either depressive or anti-social disorders, and features such as preoccupation with the image of the deceased which are characteristic of adult grief reactions (Lindemann, 1944) were almost entirely confined to this small group of children.

The mechanism of the association between bereavement and the later development of psychiatric disorder has been most systematically considered by Bowlby in a series of papers (1953, 1960, 1961a and b). He stated that the child's tie to his mother is mediated by 'instinctual response systems' (Bowlby, 1961b), and laying the emphasis on primitive biological processes, he compared mourning responses with those observed in animals. He considers that the '. . . persistent seeking of reunion with a permanently lost object is the main motivation present in pathological mourning, although it appears in forms which, because of repression and splitting, have become disguised and distorted' (Bowlby, 1961b). Thus, he believes that those bereaved when young not only develop personality disorders but are also more likely to respond to further loss by pathological mourning and so to develop psychiatric illness.

Bowlby considers that the process of mourning which follows bereavement is the key to the problem, and he regards pathological variants as commoner in early childhood. The finding that disturbances less frequently followed parental loss in the first two years of life suggests that the development of a close parent-child relationship is often necessary before a child responds adversely to the loss of a parent through death. Also too, a continuing parent-child relationship may be more important for normal development in early childhood in that the older children seemed to suffer less from loss of a parent. Before the age of 1 or 2 years the child has had less time to form a firm relationship with his parents and so will be less distressed at disruption of the relationship by death, whereas after 6 years of age he will increasingly have had a shorter period of development without a parent. There is some suggestion that in cultures where there is a less exclusive attachment to a single mother (or father) figure, parental death causes less disturbance (Waller, 1951; Volkart, 1957). However, there is little evidence to suggest that the parent-child relationship is instinctual, and Bowlby has laid greater emphasis on learning in later papers (Bowlby, 1961b). The tendency to attribute behaviour in animals to 'instinct' has come under heavy criticism in recent years (Lehrman, 1953; Schneirla, 1959) and although the concept of instinct cannot perhaps be abandoned (Thorpe, 1961), the roles of learning and habituation are clearly relevant.

There is no direct evidence that processes of mourning are more frequently pathological in childhood. That there is usually less overt grief in young children (Burlingham and Freud, 1942 and 1944; Marris, 1958) may be interpreted as meaning that the emotional disturbances are less severe, or that the absence of grief is a pathological development (Deutsch, 1937) related to failure to carry out the 'work of mourning' (Fenichel, 1945). The former is the more parsimonious explanation and in the absence of further data there is little reason to prefer the latter and more speculative inference. In view of the usually long delay between bereavement and the onset of disorder the relevant factors may lie not in the death itself or the child's grief at the time, but in subsequent events and circumstances.

Parental death was followed by break-up of the home—previously shown to be associated with the development of child psychiatric disorder—in a substantial minority. Children were sometimes subject to several changes from one makeshift arrangement to another and a few were placed in institutions. Marris (1958) found that widows' reactions to bereavement sometimes manifested themselves by indifference to their children's needs. Grief in adults is often prolonged (Marris, 1958) and for younger children the surviving parent's grief may be more adversely influential than the death itself. Poverty and loneliness for the widow often followed her husband's death and played an important role in forcing readjustments for the family (Marris, 1958). Bereavement was frequently followed by impaired relationships with the deceased husband's family (Marris, 1958) and by adjustments of roles within the immediate family (Waller, 1951). If children have to take over the role of a parent it may be difficult for them to reconcile their adult role at home with their child's role at school. Overdependence of the surviving parent on the children may lead to difficulties in adolescence when the children have to achieve independence (Hilgard et al., 1960; Marris, 1958; Waller, 1951). Remarriage, although it often eases the surviving parent's plight (Marris, 1958), tends to aggravate the children's problems of adaptation (Heilpern, 1943; Janet, 1925; Marris, 1958; Podolsky, 1955). Podolsky (1955) believed that these problems were particularly great during adolescence— when many of the bereaved children in the present study first developed symptoms.

Children grieve over the death of their parents and although this may develop into a morbid grief reaction in some older children, for younger ones pathological developments are probably more related to the consequences of death. Breakdown after bereavement in early childhood is most likely during adolescence. It was not possible in the present study to determine which consequences of parental death were most deleterious and this appears to be a fruitful area for further study.

# CHAPTER VIII

# VARIABLES INFLUENCING THE ASSOCIATION BETWEEN PSYCHIATRIC DISORDERS IN PARENTS AND THEIR CHILDREN

THE QUESTION of what kinds of mental illness in the parent or what aspects of the illness were related to psychiatric disorder in the children, will be considered in this chapter. The group of mentally ill parents will first be described as a whole, but the distribution of diagnoses or other variables in this group means little unless it can be compared with the distribution in the population of psychiatric patients from which these mentally ill patients were drawn. As explained earlier, it was not possible to do this, but the comparison could be made for those 48 parents who had themselves been treated at The Maudsley Hospital and who had first been seen as out-patients. This subgroup was therefore analysed in more detail and their characteristics were compared with a randomly selected control group of Maudsley patients who were also parents [see FIGURE 2.2, p. 23 for selection of groups].

## I. TOTAL GROUP

### Diagnosis

The mentally ill parents were subdivided according to where they had received treatment: (i) The Maudsley Hospital, (ii) mental hospital (in-patients), (iii) general hospital or private psychiatric clinic, (iv) those who had not received treatment (the suicidal group), together with those for whom the place of treatment was not known.

Present-day classification of psychiatric illness is not wholly satisfactory. Many different schemes are in use (Stengel, 1960); diagnoses lack reliability (Brooke, 1960) and are used by psychiatrists in different ways. A breakdown of diagnosis into more than broad groupings was therefore not worth while, but general groupings have a fairly satisfactory reliability (Norris, 1959) and diagnoses were accordingly grouped under five headings: schizophrenia, depression, neurosis, personality disorder, and other diagnoses.[1]

The diagnoses used were those noted in the relevant hospital records. The number of diagnoses exceeds the number of patients because if two principal diagnoses were recorded, both were used, as the decision to place one or other first was likely to have been arbitrary. Some patients were also treated at more than one hospital. Most dual diagnoses mentioned personality disorder

[1] Definitions for these terms, as used, are given in the APPENDIX.

plus some other condition, usually neurosis or depression, and by including both it was hoped to compare aspects of the psychiatric illness and pathological personality characteristics. The distribution of diagnoses is shown in TABLE 8.1.

TABLE 8.1
DIAGNOSIS OF THE PARENTS ACCORDING TO PLACE OF TREATMENT

| Diagnosis | Bethlem Maudsley (No.) | Mental hospital (No.) | General hospital or private (No.) | Not treated or place not known (No.) | Total |
|---|---|---|---|---|---|
| Schizophrenia | 5 | 9 | — | — | 11 |
| Depression | 20 | 16 | 18 | — | 43 |
| Neurosis | 20 | 10 | 21 | — | 42 |
| Personality disorder | 21 | 20 | 15 | — | 39 |
| Other | 2 | 2 | 4 | 1 | 9 |
| Suicidal act only | — | — | — | 12 | 12 |
| Not known | 2 | 5 | — | 8 | 15 |
| Total patients | 56 | 50 | 47 | 21 | 137 |

*Which Parent Ill*

The '*disturbed*' children with mentally ill parents were divided into those whose mother alone was ill, those whose father alone was ill, and those whose parents both had psychiatric disorder. The '*both*' group refers only to parents who had a mental illness as defined, and excludes parents who were referred only after the child first attended The Maudsley Hospital.

TABLE 8.2
RELATIONSHIP BETWEEN WHICH PARENT ILL AND
WHERE PARENT TREATED

| Place treated | Both | Parent ill Mother only | Father only | Total |
|---|---|---|---|---|
| Bethlem, Maudsley | 13 | 34 | 9 | 56 |
| Mental hospital | 12 | 27 | 11 | 50 |
| General hospital or private | 15 | 20 | 12 | 47 |
| Other | 1 | 6 | 9 | 16 |
| Total | 28 | 72 | 37 | 137 |
| | (20·4%) | (52·6%) | (27·0%) | |

In a strikingly high proportion of children (one in five (20·4 per cent.)), both parents had a mental illness, and the proportion with only the mother ill (52·6 per cent.) was nearly double that with only the father ill (27·0 per cent.).

The frequency with which both parents were mentally ill is shown in TABLE 8.3 by diagnosis. The relationship between the diagnoses of both partners is also shown. The incidence of illness in the spouse was similar

TABLE 8.3

RELATIONSHIP BETWEEN DIAGNOSIS OF PARENT AND PSYCHIATRIC ILLNESS IN THE SPOUSE

| Diagnosis | Total No. cases | Cases where spouse ill | Diagnosis of spouse | No. |
|---|---|---|---|---|
| Schizophrenia | 11 | — | — | — |
| Depression | 43 | 13 | Depression | 3 |
| | | | Neurosis | 3 |
| | | | Personality disorder | 4 |
| | | | Other | 1 |
| | | | Suicidal act | 3 |
| | | | Not known | 2 |
| Neurosis | 42 | 17 | Depression | 4 |
| | | | Neurosis | 7 |
| | | | Personality disorder | 6 |
| | | | Other | 1 |
| | | | Suicidal act | — |
| | | | Not known | 2 |
| Personality disorder | 39 | 13 | Depression | 4 |
| | | | Neurosis | 6 |
| | | | Personality disorder | 3 |
| | | | Other | — |
| | | | Suicidal act | — |
| | | | Not known | 2 |
| Suicidal act | 12 | 2 | Depression | 2 |
| Other | 9 | 3 | Depression | 1 |
| | | | Neurosis | 1 |
| | | | Personality disorder | 1 |
| Not known | 15 | 3 | Depression | 1 |
| | | | Neurosis | 2 |
| | | | Personality disorder | 1 |

in all diagnostic groups except that of schizophrenia, where it did not occur at all. The diagnoses of the two parents, where both were ill, bore little relationship to each other. These findings are in general agreement with the only other comparable studies in the literature (Kreitman, 1962; Nielson, 1964). Kreitman, in his study of all new referrals to the Chichester Psychiatric Service between 1958 and 1960, found only one case of schizophrenia out of 21 husband and wife pairs in which both partners were ill (i.e. 42 patients); concordance of diagnosis occurred in only 29 per cent. of the pairs. Nielson (1964) in a study of mental disorder on the island of Samsø also found no schizophrenics in his husband and wife pairs where both were ill; concordance of diagnosis occurred in 38 per cent. of the pairs, or 52 per cent. if neurosis and character disorder are taken together and psychogenic and endogenous depression together.

*In-patient or Out-patient Care*

In 71 of the 137 children with mentally ill parents at least one parent had received in-patient care.

## II. MAUDSLEY PATIENTS

Of the total number of mentally ill parents 56 had been Maudsley Hospital patients and 48 of these first attended as out-patients. The illnesses of these 48 parents were compared in detail with those of a random sample of other Maudsley patients. The method of obtaining this control sample was outlined in CHAPTER II. Thus, the 48 mentally ill parents of Maudsley 'disturbed' children (group 1) were compared with the 169 Maudsley patients who had children who were well (group 2). All tests of significance apply only to differences between these groups but the data for the 31 Maudsley patients (from the random control sample) whose children had psychiatric disorder (group 3) are also given.

*Sex of the Mentally Ill Parent*

TABLE 8.4

SEX OF MENTALLY ILL PARENT AND DISORDER IN THE CHILD

| Sex | Group (key below) | | |
|---|---|---|---|
| | *1* | *2* | *3* |
| | No. % | No. % | No. % |
| Male | 13 (27·1) | 83 (49·1) | 7 (22·6) |
| Female | 35 (72·9) | 86 (50·9) | 24 (77·4) |
| Total | 48 | 169 | 31 |

Chi-square = 7·365   1 d.f.   p<0·01

KEY:   1—Parents of the children attending The Maudsley Hospital (study group)

2—Control group—parents with 'normal' children

3—Control group—parents with psychiatrically ill children

There was a significant but not large excess of mentally ill mothers among the mentally ill parents of 'disturbed' children, 72·9 per cent. compared with 50·9 per cent. in the control group, and the control group parents with mentally ill children contained three times as many mothers as fathers. Psychiatric illness in the mother was therefore more often associated with disorder in the child than was illness in the father. If the psychiatrist treating the parent was more likely to inquire about disorder in the children when it was the mother who was ill, this could explain the association within the control group, though it could not in the study group cases. Alternatively, mentally ill mothers might be unduly concerned about possible behaviour abnormalities in their children and so present them for psychiatric treatment more readily than do normal mothers, while this would not apply to fathers, as most fathers have less to do with the care of the children. This was unlikely to be an important cause of bias, as disorders in the children of mentally ill parents were more severe than, and lasted as long as, those in the children of parents who had no mental illness.

Among the whole group only twice could a mentally ill parent have been said to use the child as a presenting symptom: A severely deluded schizo-phrenic mother came to the Department with very vague complaints about her son, and it seemed probable that this was a reflection of a relapse in her own illness. However, though her other children appeared normal, the one she brought to the Department did have a behaviour disorder. The other was a neurotic mother whose one child was already having treatment at The Maudsley Hospital. She then brought up her other child, a boy of two years. It was decided at the clinic that he was a normal child, although, because of the mother's illness, the relationship between the child and his mother was severely disturbed. Accordingly, the case was included in the *non-disturbed* rather than *disturbed* group.

The excess of mothers was also found in the parents who attended hospitals other than the Maudsley. However, as there is a marked preponderance of women among married patients admitted to mental hospitals (Brooke, 1961) it is uncertain whether the excess of mothers among parents treated else-where was greater than would be expected by chance.

### Age

There was no consistent trend in the age differences between the groups [TABLE 8.5 in the APPENDIX]; it was concluded that the parent's age did not differentiate patients with psychiatrically ill children from those with normal children.

### Social Class

There was no consistent trend in social class differences (*Registrar General's Classification*) between the groups [TABLE 8.6 in the APPENDIX].

### Number of Children

There were slightly fewer parents of only children in the study group ($p < 0.04$) and rather more with three or more children (difference not signi-ficant) but this difference was not reflected in the parents with psychiatrically ill children from within the control group. The slight differences were thus probably unimportant.

### In- and Out-patient Care

The groups did not differ according to the proportion receiving in-patient care [TABLE 8.7 in the APPENDIX].

### Duration of Parental Illness

The parents of Maudsley *disturbed* children had fewer illnesses lasting less than a year and more of longer duration; the difference was probably significant ($p < 0.05$). This was not found in the control group parents with psychiatrically ill children and so must be accepted with caution, though it is consonant with the view that chronic parental illnesses would carry a greater association with disorder in the children. However, the data refer only to duration of symptoms before attendance at hospital and are only indirectly relevant to the more important questions of total duration of parental disorder, which could not be compared between the two groups.

TABLE 8.8

DURATION OF SYMPTOMS OF THE MENTALLY ILL PARENT
AND DISORDER IN THE CHILD

| Duration of Symptoms | Groups | | |
|---|---|---|---|
| | *1* | *2* | *3* |
| | *No.* % | *No.* % | *No.* % |
| Less than 1 year | 11 *(22·9)* | 75 *(44·4)* | 12 *(38·7)* |
| 1 year but less than 3 | 16 *(33·3)* | 40 *(23·7)* | 8 *(25·8)* |
| 3 years or longer | 21 *(43·8)* | 46 *(27·2)* | 8 *(25·8)* |
| Total | 48 | 161 | 28 |
| Not known | | 8 | 3 |

Chi-square = 8·625   2 d.f.   p<0·05

*Diagnosis of the Mentally Ill Parent*

The diagnoses of the study and control groups were grouped into five broad categories as before [TABLE 8.9].

TABLE 8.9

PARENTAL DIAGNOSIS AND DISORDER IN THE CHILD

| Diagnosis | Groups | | | Significance Critical ratio | *p* |
|---|---|---|---|---|---|
| | *1* | *2* | *3* | | |
| | *No.* % | *No.* % | *No.* % | | |
| Neurosis | 19 *(39·6)* | 67 *(39·6)* | 9 *(29·0)* | N.S. | |
| Depression | 19 *(39·6)* | 55 *(32·5)* | 18 *(58·1)* | N.S. | |
| Schizophrenia | 2 *(4·2)* | 19 *(11·2)* | 0 — | N.S. | |
| Personality disorder | 16 *(33·3)* | 33 *(19·5)* | 10 *(32·2)* | 2·06 | <0·04 |
| Other | 1 *(2·1)* | 11 *(6·5)* | 1 *(3·2)* | N.S. | |
| Total no. of patients | 48 | 169 | 31 | | |

A third of the parents with psychiatrically ill children (33·3 per cent.) had received the diagnosis of personality disorder compared with only one in five (19·5 per cent.) of those with children who were well. The difference was probably significant (p<0·04) and a similar difference was also found within the control group between those whose children were ill and those whose children were well (i.e. between groups 3 and 2). Personality disorder implies a lifelong abnormality particularly associated with difficulties in interpersonal relationships that could be expected to affect the harmony of the home and hence the children's adjustment. Blacker (1958) found that personality disorder was twice as often associated with a broken marriage— separation, divorce, etc.—as any other diagnosis, and broken marriages have already been shown, in this study and others, to be associated with psychiatric disorder in the children (the association is probably related to conditions accompanying the 'break-up' rather than to the disruption itself). It will be shown in the next chapter that the mentally ill parents showed a relationship similar (although less marked) to that reported by Blacker between diagnosis and break-up of marriage.

Rather surprisingly, the study and control groups did not differ significantly in frequency of broken marriages (12·5 per cent. in the study and 11·2 per cent. in the control group), though the parents with mentally ill children within the control group (group 3) did differ (29·0 per cent.). The probable explanation is that in the control group the children were already disturbed when the parent attended hospital, or became so during the period of treatment, so that causal factors could be assumed to be already operating. On the other hand, most children in the study group did not develop disorder until later. Thus, the time relationships differed between the two groups; moreover, many more of the study group marriages ended in separation or divorce *after* the parent first attended The Maudsley Hospital but *before* the child did so.

The proportions of other diagnoses did not differ significantly between the groups, but fewer than one in twenty of the parents in the study group had schizophrenia, whereas the proportion in the control group was more than double this. The number of patients was too small for this difference to reach significance but the direction of the difference is in keeping with other studies which found that the children of schizophrenics are not a high risk group (see for example Cowie, 1961a and b and Sunier and Meijers, 1951).

## Symptoms of the Parental Illness

The symptoms described in the hospital notes of the patients were grouped into 12 categories,[1] and defined as either present or absent. The groups are not mutually exclusive, as patients might have symptoms in several different categories.

Affective symptoms (anxiety and depression) occurred more frequently in the parents of Maudsley *'disturbed'* children than in the control group, but only the difference for anxiety symptoms reached significance ($p<0·01$). Somatic symptoms, also more frequent in the study group ($p<0·01$), consisted mainly of depressive hypochondriacal symptoms. Fabian and Donohue (1956) had previously considered that parental depressive illness was particularly likely to be associated with disorder in the children, probably because depression often caused feelings of hostility to the child.

The most striking difference between the groups was the large and significant ($p<0·00001$) excess, in the study group, of parental symptoms which directly involved the child (52·1 per cent. compared with 8·3 per cent. in the control group). There was a smaller but still significant ($p<0·01$) excess of symptoms directly involving the spouse (39·6 per cent. compared with 19·5 per cent.). Both differences appeared to a similar extent between the parents

---

[1] Definitions are given in the APPENDIX.

TABLE 8.10

PARENTAL SYMPTOMS AND DISORDER IN THE CHILD

| Symptoms | Groups | | | | | | Significance Critical ratio | p |
|---|---|---|---|---|---|---|---|---|
| | 1 | | 2 | | 3 | | | |
| | No. | % | No. | % | No. | % | | |
| Anxiety | 34 | (70·7) | 83 | (49·1) | 17 | (44·8) | 2·67 | <0·01 |
| Depression | 36 | (75·0) | 106 | (62·7) | 24 | (77·4) | N.S. | |
| Delusions | 6 | (12·5) | 27 | (16·0) | 1 | (3·2) | N.S. | |
| Hallucinations | — | — | 10 | (5·9) | 1 | (3·2) | N.S. | |
| Obsessional | 2 | (4·2) | 13 | (7·7) | 1 | (3·2) | N.S. | |
| Hysterical | 4 | (8·3) | 11 | (6·5) | 3 | (9·7) | N.S. | |
| Somatic | 24 | (50·0) | 47 | (27·8) | 7 | (22·6) | 2·707 | <0·01 |
| Suicidal acts or gestures | 11 | (22·9) | 21 | (12·4) | 5 | (16·1) | N.S. | |
| Other | 3 | (6·3) | 18 | (10·7) | 3 | (9·7) | N.S. | |
| Involving spouse | 19 | (39·6) | 33 | (19·5) | 15 | (48·4) | 2·913 | <0·01 |
| Involving children | 25 | (52·1) | 14 | (8·3) | 15 | (48·4) | 7·065 | <0·00001 |
| Involving others | — | — | 11 | (6·5) | 2 | (6·5) | N.S. | |
| Total parents | 48 | | 169 | | 31 | | | |

whose children were well (group 2) and those whose children were ill (group 3) within the control group. The disorders with symptoms directly involving the children were heterogeneous and included all diagnostic categories. Of the total study group of patient-parents of Maudsley children (i.e. the 89 attending hospitals other than the Maudsley as well as the 48 attending The Maudsley Hospital), thirteen were overtly hostile towards their children; another seven had actually attacked the child and six others had impulses to harm their offspring. Other types of symptom which involved the child included morbid beliefs that the child was defective, illegitimate, or else abnormal since birth because of rubella during pregnancy. A few parents had depressive ideas of self-blame about the child and one believed that she had harmed the child through lack of care. Delusions involved a few children; one parent believed that he could influence his child by wiggling his toes and another that the child could influence her. One mother forced her child to perform her obsessional rituals and several were irritable with their children or morbidly anxious about them. The impact of the symptoms varied in setting and in intensity but what seemed important was not so much the formal diagnosis or symptomatology, as that the symptoms directly involved the child, often with overt or covert hostile feelings.

When patients with symptoms which directly involved the child were excluded and the groups again compared, there was no longer any difference regarding anxiety symptoms but otherwise the differences were not greatly altered. The numbers were too small for valid conclusions.

The frequency of symptoms involving the children was remarkable and important. Nevertheless, a caveat is necessary, in spite of the high degree of statistical significance. The comparison refers only to parents attending The Maudsley Hospital and it is not known whether the finding applies to patients who attended other hospitals. Examination of the records suggested that it did apply to patients of all hospitals and clinics, but no appropriate control group was available. Also, certain sources of error were implicit in the method of recording the data. Independent and blind ratings were not used, as this part of the study was exploratory, and, although terms were defined and every effort was made to be impartial, bias may still have operated in the author's recording of symptoms. (On the other hand, this finding had not been expected when the study was begun). If the child was already overtly disturbed (as was sometimes the case), the clinician treating the parent may have paid greater attention to symptoms which involved the child and so noted them more frequently. If the child's behaviour was creating difficulties in the home at the time the parent attended hospital, the parent-patient may have been more likely to focus upon the child anxiety, hostility, guilt or other existing symptoms. Any of these potential sources of error may have caused a statistically significant but factitious difference. Close examination of the case histories suggested that this was not usually so and that the association was probably a real one, but the matter can only be conclusively decided by a prospective study designed to test the association.

### Psychiatric Illness in the Spouse

The frequency with which the spouse had also had a mental illness (as defined) is compared between the groups in TABLE 8.11.

TABLE 8.11
PSYCHIATRIC ILLNESS IN THE SPOUSE AND DISORDER IN THE CHILD

| Psychiatric illness in the spouse | Groups | | | Significance Critical ratio | $p$ |
|---|---|---|---|---|---|
| | 1 | 2 | 3 | | |
| | No. % | No. % | No. % | | |
| Spouse ill | 14 (29·1) | 5 (3·0) | 6 (19·4) | 5·8 | <0·00001 |
| Spouse not ill | 34 | 164 | 25 | | |
| Total | 48 | 169 | 31 | | |

Among the parents whose children were also patients, in nearly a third (29·1 per cent.) *both* parents were ill, compared with less than one in thirty (3·0 per cent.) in the control group; the difference was highly significant (p<0·00001). The study and control groups were not strictly comparable, however. For the parents of Maudsley children data regarding illness in either parent, irrespective of which parent became ill first were available up to the time of the child's attendance. On the other hand, for the control group, although previous or existing psychiatric illness in the spouse was probably recorded, if the spouse *later* developed a psychiatric illness, usually this was recorded in the first set of notes only if the first parent was still attending. Thus, as the ages of the patients in the two groups were comparable, assuming that other things were equal, the true proportion of mentally ill spouses in the control group might be anything up to double the recorded figures, i.e. up to

6 per cent. This is still only a fifth of the proportion in the study group and so the possible artifact is unlikely to account for the difference, especially as a similar, but slightly smaller, difference was found in the control group with mentally ill children (group 3).

The eventual proportions of patients whose husband or wife has also been a patient would, of course, be much higher, as the association is dependent on the ages of the people concerned. The proportions compared are only relevant for this particular age group, but the difference between the groups is very large and highly significant.

The finding is not surprising because if a parental psychiatric illness is harmful for the children, the effect is presumably greater when both parents are ill, through summation of influences (whether environmental or genetic). Moreover, if the illness is harmful to the child by impairing parental functioning, the effect would be greater when there is not a healthy parent to take over the role of the sick member. The importance of the spouse in this respect has been noted by several writers (Sunier and Meijers, 1951; Lane, 1956; Sussex, 1963; Sussex et al., 1963; Ekdahl et al., 1962) who emphasized the increased problems of adaptation for the family when the other parent is either absent or too disturbed to take over the responsibilities of the sick parent. If the effect of parental illness on the child is through genetic transmission of psychopathological traits, the effect would be much increased by illness in both parents. On the other hand, the illnesses in father and mothers were usually dissimilar so that the genetic factors of each could not necessarily be assumed to add to the effect of the other. The extent to which the association between illnesses in parents and in their children was hereditary is discussed more fully in CHAPTER X.

In the parents treated at hospitals other than the Maudsley, there was also a high incidence of psychiatric illness in the spouse (20·4 per cent. in the whole group of parents, excluding cases where the spouse was first treated after the child first attended The Maudsley Hospital, and for those treated at mental hospitals the figure was 24 per cent.). The available figures for the general population of psychiatric patients are not strictly comparable. The *Registrar General's Statistical Review for 1949* (but not since) gave the number of partners of ever-married patients who had suffered from a mental illness dealt with under the Mental Treatment Act, but there was no information on those who had received treatment outside the Act. The proportions were 112 per 6,600 males for whom the information was available and 110 per 6,478 females similarly. Both figures are well below those of the present study. Slightly more comparable are the figures for patients attending the Chichester and District Psychiatric Service between 1958 and 1960 inclusive (Kreitman, 1962). Out of 1,347 new referrals of married men and women during this period in only 21 marriages were both partners seen, about 1½ per cent. Although neither the Registrar General's nor Kreitman's figures are comparable to those in the present study the difference is large enough to suggest that the significant excess of illness in both parents of mentally ill children found in parents treated at The Maudsley Hospital probably applies also to those treated elsewhere.

Apart from Sobel's study (1961) of the children of schizophrenics, there appear to be no other studies of child psychiatric disorder in the offspring of parents both of whom have mental illness, although careful studies of the adult psychiatric states of such children have been reported (Lewis, 1957).

*Factors in the Child*

The features of the parental mental illness associated with disorder in the child have already been noted. It has also been shown that child psychiatric disorder was frequently present in several children in the family. Nevertheless, about half the children of mentally-ill parents had not developed any disorder and the question remained: in what way did these children differ from those who were psychiatrically ill?

The entire sibships of the '*disturbed*' children with psychiatrically ill parents were divided into three parts: (*a*) the propositi, (*b*) the sibs with psychiatric disorder (as defined) and (*c*) the sibs without psychiatric disorder. The first two groups were then combined into a group of mentally ill children which was compared with the third group of children who were well. The sex distribution in the groups is shown in TABLE 8.12.

TABLE 8.12
SEXES OF CHILDREN WHO WERE ILL AND THOSE WHO WERE NOT ILL

| | *Groups* | | | | | |
| --- | --- | --- | --- | --- | --- | --- |
| | *Children with Psychiatric Disorder* | | | | | |
| *Sex* | *Propositi* | *Sibs* | *Total* | | *Other Sibs* | |
| | *No.* | *No.* | *No.* | *%* | *No.* | *%* |
| Male | 82 | 31 | 113 | *(61·8)* | 94 | *(50·8)* |
| Female | 55 | 15 | 70 | *(38·2)* | 91 | *(49·2)* |
| Total | 137 | 46 | 183 | | 185 | |

Chi-square = 4·470   1 d.f.   p<0·05

The psychiatrically ill children were more often boys than girls (61·8 per cent. boys and 38·2 per cent. girls), whereas among the mentally healthy sibs the sex distribution was about equal; the difference between the groups was probably significant (p<0·05). The excess of boys in the psychiatrically ill group was similar to that in the clinic as a whole and probably reflects the generally greater susceptibility to psychiatric disorders shown by boys.

The children's ages were compared at two points in time in relation to the parental illness: (*a*) the parent's first attendance at any psychiatric clinic, and (*b*) the estimated time when symptoms first began (on average, this was about two years earlier).

The children who developed psychiatric disorder were more likely to have been alive when the parent first attended a psychiatric clinic (84·2 per cent. compared with 62·2 per cent. of the sibs who remained well), and, of

## TABLE 8.13
### AGE OF CHILDREN WHEN PARENT FIRST ATTENDED A PSYCHIATRIC CLINIC

| | Propositi with Psychiatric Disorder No. | Sibs with Psychiatric Disorder No. | Total No. % | Other Sibs No. % | Significance Critical ratio | p |
|---|---|---|---|---|---|---|
| *Groups* | | | | | | |
| *Ages* | | | | | | |
| Not born | 18 | 11 | 29 (*15·8*) | 70 (*37·8*) | 3·27 | <0·01 |
| Total No. Children | 137 | 46 | 183 | 185 | | |
| | | | % of those born | % of those born | | |
| Less than 2 years | 18 | 6 | 24 (*15·6*) | 18 (*15·6*) | | |
| 2–3 years | 22 | 6 | 28 (*18·2*) | 17 (*14·8*) | | |
| 4–5 years | 19 | 6 | 25 (*16·2*) | 20 (*17·4*) | | |
| 6–7 years | 19 | 6 | 25 (*16·2*) | 25 (*21·7*) | | |
| 8–9 years | 15 | 5 | 20 (*13·0*) | 9 (*7·8*) | | |
| 10–11 years | 16 | 2 | 18 (*11·7*) | 8 (*7·0*) | | |
| 12–13 years | 6 | 4 | 10 (*6·5*) | 8 (*7·0*) | | |
| 14–15 years | 3 | — | 3 (*2·0*) | 4 (*3·5*) | 2·26 | <0·03 |
| 16 years or older | 1 | — | 1 (*0·6*) | 6 (*5·2*) | | |
| Total of those born | 119 | 35 | 154 | 115 | | |

(With division of groups into three parts; children not born, children aged 13 years or younger, and children aged 14 years or older, a chi-square test was performed)

Chi-square = 26·2305    2 d.f.    p<0·001

those alive, more of the mentally ill children were then under 14 years of age. Both differences were significant. Similar differences were found when the ages of the children were compared at the time the parent first developed symptoms, and again were significant. When the parent first became ill, only 6·7 per cent. of the mentally ill children were 12 years or older compared with 17·3 per cent. of the children who remained well (as onset preceded referral by two years on average, the age of differentiation was necessarily also two years earlier).

Thus, age at the time of the parental illness differentiated the mentally ill children from those who were well, but only within very broad limits. The adolescents were somewhat less likely to become ill after the parental disorder. It may be that personality development is more stable by then so that older children tend to break down less easily in response to family stresses. At the other end of the age range more of the mentally ill children were born at the time the parent first became ill. Thus, the children who remained well tended either to be adolescent or very young during their parent's illness or not to have been born until afterwards. If the deleterious effects of parental mental

G

TABLE 8.14

## AGE OF CHILDREN AT POINT OF ONSET OF PARENTAL SYMPTOMS

| Ages | Propositi with Psychiatric Disorder No. | Sibs with Psychiatric Disorder No. | Total No.  % | Other Sibs No.  % | Significance Critical ratio | p |
|---|---|---|---|---|---|---|
| Not born | 50 | 28 | 78 (42·6) | 98 (53·0) | 2·00 | <0·05 |
| Total No. Children | 137 | 46 | 183 | 185 | | |
| | | | % of those born | % of those born | | |
| Less than 2 years | 10 | 5 | 15 (14·3) | 11 (12·6) | | |
| 2–3 years | 21 | 2 | 23 (21·9) | 12 (13·8) | | |
| 4–5 years | 11 | 4 | 15 (14·3) | 16 (18·4) | | |
| 6–7 years | 16 | 2 | 18 (17·1) | 20 (23·0) | | |
| 8–9 years | 12 | 4 | 16 (15·2) | 7 (8·0) | | |
| 10–11 years | 10 | 1 | 11 (10·5) | 6 (6·9) | | |
| 12–13 years | 3 | — | 3 (2·9) | 7 (8·1) | | |
| 14–15 years | 3 | — | 3 (2·9) | 4 (4·6) | 2·304 | <0·03 |
| 16 years or older | 1 | — | 1 (0·9) | 4 (4·6) | | |
| Total of those born | 87 | 18 | 105 | 87 | | |

*Groups*

(With division of groups into three parts; children not born, children aged 11 years or younger, and children aged 12 years or older, a chi-square test was performed)

Chi-square = 9·145   2 d.f.   p<0·01

illness were environmental rather than genetic in action, this finding was logical.

It should also be noted, however, that the children not yet born when the parents became ill were necessarily younger at the time of the study. Another explanation for the age difference between the groups would be that sibs who were well were well simply because they were too young for the psychiatric disorder to manifest itself. This may have been so in some instances but, in fact, the mentally ill children were on average younger than the rest of the clinic population and some were very young (10 per cent. were five years or younger).

## Discussion and Conclusions

The relationship between the diagnosis of the parental illness and the likelihood of psychiatric disorder in the children was not strong. But, parents with abnormalities of personality most often had children with neurotic or behavioural disorders. On the other hand, only a few schizophrenics had disturbed children (although this difference did not reach an acceptable level of statistical significance). Thus, the 'severity' of the parental illness did not seem to be important (if a psychotic illness like schizophrenia can be considered more severe than neurotic or personality disorders). This finding is in keeping with findings elsewhere. The children of psychotic parents were generally well-adjusted in the early studies of Canavan and Clark (1923a and b; 1936), Ramage (1925), and Preston and Antin (1933). Their findings were confirmed by the better controlled investigations of Sunier and Meijers (1951) and Cowie (1961a and b). Most of the parents of neurotic children in Buck and Laughton's study (1959) were neurotic rather than psychotic. Kellner (1963) described associations between neurosis in parents and their children, and Janet (1925) and Huschka (1941) noted neurotic and affective disorder among the parents of neurotic children rather than psychoses. Similarly, Post (1962) found psychiatric disorders to be commonest in the children of parents with chronic or recurrent affective and neurotic disorders. Many children of neurotics may be normal (Macdonald, 1939) but, in general, disorders in the child are associated with parental neurosis or psychopathy rather than psychosis. The form of the parental illness may not necessarily be the relevant differentiating feature. Schizophrenia, where the rate of disorder in the children has been found to be low, differs markedly from other mental disorders on at least three other variables, two of which are known to be associated with the development of psychiatric disorder in children. These are: (1) the frequency with which mental illness occurs in *both* parents; (2) breakdown of the marriage; (3) admission to hospital.

In the present study, one of the largest and most striking differences between parents whose children were ill and those whose children were well was the incidence of psychiatric disorder in both parents. Among the Maudsley patients who were parents of children attending the psychiatric clinic, in nearly a third of cases both parents were patients, and in the whole group of children with mentally ill parents, one child in five had both parents ill. In sharp contrast, this occurred in less than one in thirty of the control group of parent-patients. However, *none* of the spouses of schizophrenic patients was ill. Similarly, in Kreitman's study (1962) of pairs in which both husband and wife were psychiatric patients, only one patient out of 42 was diagnosed as schizophrenic. This appears low, but the proportion of schizophrenics in the patient population from which they were drawn was not given. In the present study, most schizophrenics had a mentally healthy spouse who could look after the children. Again, Sunier and Meijer's finding of a low rate of disorder in the children of schizophrenics applied only to couples in which the non-psychotic spouse showed no psychiatric abnormality. Sussex (Sussex, 1963; Sussex et al., 1963), too, found that when the other parent was unable to look after the children, the children of schizophrenics more often became maladjusted. Similarly, Sobel (1961) found that of four children cared for by two parents both of whom were psychotic, three showed abnormalities in infancy. The relatively low rate of psychiatric disorder in the children of schizophrenics may thus be due to the fact that, unlike the situation with neurotics and psychopaths, the schizophrenic's spouse is usually healthy and able to cope with the children.

Many studies have shown a relationship between break-up of the marriage and the development of psychiatric disorder in the children but, at least in hospital groups studied in the past, schizophrenics have differed from other psychiatric patients in having a low rate of separation and divorce (Blacker, 1958) and this may also be related to the low rate of disorder in the children. Again the important factor may be the continuing presence of a parent who can care for the children when the other parent is ill or in hospital (Ekdahl et al., 1962). Recent unpublished studies of schizophrenic patients in mental hospitals (Brown, personal communication) have found much higher rates of divorce than those given by Blacker (1958). This difference in divorce rates of schizophrenics may be due to differences in the social background of the schizophrenics in each sample but may also reflect a real change in recent years, perhaps related to the change in patterns of psychiatric care. If there has been a real change in the rate of marriage breakdown in schizophrenics, it might be associated with an increased rate of psychiatric disorder in the children.

The third main difference between schizophrenics and other psychiatric patients lies in the hospital experience of the two groups. Until the last decade (and most studies of the children of schizophrenics stem from an earlier period), schizophrenics were usually admitted to hospitals where they might remain for many years. There was thus little contact between the psychotic parent and his family. Though patients with other diagnoses were sometimes admitted to hospital, the majority were discharged much earlier. The last few years, however, have seen major changes in the patterns of psychiatric care in this country, especially for the patient with a chronic illness. More schizophrenics are treated in the community, where they are in contact with their families. Also, those who are admitted to hospital now tend to have multiple short admissions with intervening periods at home (Brown et al., 1961). Ekdahl and her colleagues (1962) found that difficulties in arranging for the care of children were greater when parents kept going in and out of hospital than when they went in once for a longer period. Also, the schizophrenics treated at home are often so disturbed that relationships in the family are strained to the limits of tolerance (Wing et al., 1964). We do not yet know whether this increased burden on the families of schizophrenics means that statements concerning the low risk of disorder in their children now need to be modified.

Thus, mental illnesses which differ in their association with psychiatric disorder in the children, also differ in their association with other variables related to the risk of disorder in the children. The number of patients in the present study was too small to disentangle this complex net of relationships and we do not know with certainty which factors in the parental illness determine whether the children will develop psychopathology.

Nevertheless, the most striking feature of illnesses in the parents of children attending The Maudsley Hospital was the great frequency with which symptoms of the parental illness directly involved the child. The incidence of symptoms of this kind exceeded the rate in the control group of parent-patients to a highly significant extent. The symptoms were heterogeneous, both in origin and in the form and intensity of their impact on the child. A few children were victims of aggressive acts, others were subject to hostile behaviour from their parents, and many suffered from their parents' morbid anxiety or irritability. Some were the target of parental delusions, some were neglected for pathological reasons and one child had to perform obsessional rituals with his mother. Symptoms directly involving the spouse were also important. As already pointed out, for methodological reasons, caution should be exercised before accepting the size of the difference between the study and control groups in respect of the frequency with which children were involved in their parents' symptoms. Nevertheless, in many cases, the morbid behaviour associated with parental mental illness directly involved the child.

This was also prominent in Ekdahl's study of mental patients admitted to hospital (Ekdahl et al., 1962). Children had been neglected, threatened, assaulted, and sexually attacked in some cases and as in the present study, the problems associated with chronic illness were often similar whether the illness was mental or physical, but the direct involvement of the children in psychological disorders was a prominent differentiating feature.

Unfortunately, the characteristics of parental physical illness which determined the association with disorder in the children could not be studied in detail in the present study. The physical illnesses in the parents of mentally ill children were especially those which had lasted for more than a year. These chronic disorders were sometimes accompanied by mental disturbance and often ended in death. Economic difficulties were occasionally severe and some illnesses had been accompanied by breakdown in the marriage. Ekdahl has demonstrated the family stresses associated with the admission to hospital of one parent (Ekdahl et al., 1962) and Eisenberg (1960) stated that: '. . . behavioural consequences depend upon the extent to which the illness impairs the general life-energy available in the person, restricts his social role, and influences the attitudes of others towards him. Insufficient attention has been paid to the impact of illness on family equilibrium.' The literature is not very helpful in delineating those elements of physical illness which especially tax the resilience of the family unit. Although much has been written on the psychic effects of somatic illness, few conclusions can be drawn (Barker et al., 1953). Less still is known of the influence on others of physical illness in one member. The degree to which it is associated with mental abnormality may be one factor; the effect on socio-economic function is probably another. Other variables remain largely unexplored.

Only a limited examination could be made of the characteristics of the children that determined their reaction to the parental mental illness. Boys, alive but not yet adolescent at the time of the parental illness, were most likely to develop disorder. Age did not seem to be as important as it was with parental death, but whether this was because death and illness imposed different types of stress on the child of whether it was because the exact timing of parental death was much easier than the timing of illnesses which were characteristically recurrent or chronic could not be determined. Nevertheless, both with death and illness the younger child was the one most at risk and the adolescent appeared best able to withstand the stresses.

It had been hoped to relate the personality of the children to the development of psychiatric disorder in relation to parental illness. Unfortunately, data on temperament in the hospital notes varied in quantity and quality and the records did not allow any meaningful analysis of temperamental characteristics. Nevertheless, the work of Thomas, Chess, Birch and their associates (Chess et al., 1960 and 1963; Rutter et al., 1964; Thomas et al., 1961) show that reaction patterns, which have been present since infancy, determine to some extent which youngsters develop behavioural disorders and how children react to family stresses. Personality variables were probably important in determining how children reacted to parental death or illness, but they have yet to be studied.

# CHAPTER IX

# RELATIONSHIPS BETWEEN THE FORM OF ILLNESS IN THE PARENT AND THE FORM OF DISORDER IN THE CHILD

A STATISTICAL association between illnesses in parents and disorders in their children has been shown, and some characteristics of the parents and children which determined the association have been described. It remains to find out whether the form of parental illness was related to the form of the child's disorder.

*Diagnosis of Parental Mental Illness and Diagnosis of the Child's Disorder*

Of the 165 parents with psychiatric illness, no precise diagnosis was available for 15, in 9 the clinic or psychiatrist could not be traced (often because the father had had treatment while in the armed forces), and in 6 the hospital confirmed that the patient had attended for psychiatric treatment but the records could not be found. In a further 24, although a diagnosis was available, there was not enough information to list symptoms. Of these, 12 were suicidal acts, and in the remainder the records were incomplete or inadequate. In the majority of cases, however, detailed information was available.

TABLE 9.1

RELATIONSHIP BETWEEN THE DIAGNOSES OF PARENT AND CHILD

| | *Diagnoses of Children (key below)* | | | | |
|---|---|---|---|---|---|
| *Diagnosis of parents* | *N.I.* | *N.B.D.* | *M.B.D.* | *C.B.D.* | *Total* |
| Schizophrenia | 3 | 3 | 1 | 4 | 11 |
| Depression | 7 | 14 | 8 | 14 | 43 |
| Neurosis | 6 | 15 | 5 | 16 | 42 |
| Personality disorder | 4 | 10 | 13 | 12 | 39 |
| Suicide | 3 | 1 | 3 | 5 | 12 |
| Other | 1 | 5 | 2 | 1 | 9 |
| Not known | 2 | 5 | 2 | 6 | 15 |

KEY: N.I. = Neurotic illness
N.B.D. = Neurotic behaviour disorder
M.B.D. = Mixed behaviour disorder
C.B.D. = Conduct behaviour disorder (including delinquency)

The distribution of children's diagnoses was remarkably similar in all the parental diagnostic groups except that in the case of parents with a personality disorder more children were diagnosed as having a 'mixed behaviour disorder'. When personality disorders were compared with the combined other diagnoses the difference was significant ($p < 0.01$). A third of the children in the former group had a mixed behaviour disorder compared with only one in nine (11·2 per cent.) of the remainder. No other differences were statistically significant and overall there was little association between the parents' and children's diagnoses. The relationship was much less marked than, for instance, that between anomalous parenthood and conduct disorder in the child.

TABLE 9.2

RELATIONSHIP BETWEEN ANOMALOUS PARENTS AND DIAGNOSIS OF CHILD

| | | | *Diagnosis of Children* | | | | |
|---|---|---|---|---|---|---|---|
| | *N.I.* | *N.B.D.* | *Combined Neurotic*<br>*No.   %* | *M.B.D.* | *C.B.D.* | *Combined Conduct*<br>*No.   %* | *Total* |
| Anomalous parents | 5 | 8 | 13 (*26·0*) | 14 | 23 | 37 (*74·0*) | 50 |
| Other parents | 16 | 35 | 51 (*58·6*) | 10 | 26 | 36 (*41·4*) | 87 |
| Total | 21 | 43 | 64 | 24 | 49 | 73 | 137 |

Three-quarters (74·0 per cent.) of the children with anomalous parents had either a mixed or a conduct disorder compared with only one in four (26·0 per cent.) of children living with their two natural parents. Thus, as found in other studies, there was a highly significant ($p < 0·001$) relationship between anomalous parenthood (or 'broken homes') and type of disorder in the child. Blacker's (1958) finding that patients with personality disorder more often than other patients had a broken marriage, raised the possibility that the relationship between personality disorder in the parent and mixed behaviour disorder in the child might be only secondary to an increased proportion of anomalous parents among those diagnosed as having a personality disorder. The relationship between anomalous parents (as assessed at the time of the child's first attendance at The Maudsley Hospital) and parental diagnosis was therefore examined [TABLE 9.3].

With the exception of parents who had attempted or committed suicide, the proportion of anomalous parents was greatest when the parent had a personality disorder. When this diagnosis was compared with all others combined the difference fell only just short of significance (on a 2-tailed test). Half the children (48·7 per cent.) had anomalous parents where the parent had a personality disorder, as against a third of the remainder (31·6 per cent.). As the trend was in the expected direction, the relationship between parental diagnosis and the child's diagnosis was re-examined, with anomalous parenthood held constant. The relationship between personality disorder and mixed behaviour disorder remained [TABLE 9.4]. The association was significant ($p < 0·02$) for those with anomalous parents but not for children living with their two natural parents; the relative proportions in the latter group were similar but the numbers were much smaller.

As shown earlier, the diagnosis of mixed behaviour disorder reflected the

TABLE 9.3
ANOMALOUS PARENTS AND PARENTAL DIAGNOSIS

| Parental diagnosis | Anomalous parents No. % | Other parents No. | Total |
|---|---|---|---|
| Schizophrenia | 3 (27·3) | 8 | 11 |
| Depression | 14 (32·6) | 29 | 43 |
| Neurosis | 12 (28·6) | 30 | 42 |
| Personality disorder | 19 (48·7) | 20 | 39 |
| Suicidal act | 10 (83·3) | 2 | 12 |
| Other | 1 (10·0) | 9 | 10 |
| Not known | 4 (16·7) | 11 | 15 |
| Personality disorder compared with other diagnoses: | | | |
| Personality disorder | 19 (48·7) | 20 | 39 |
| Other | 31 (31·6) | 67 | 98 |

Chi-square = 3·519   0·05<p<0·1
(To reach significance a chi-square of 3·84 required)

TABLE 9.4
RELATIONSHIP BETWEEN DIAGNOSES OF CHILD AND OF PARENT
(with variable of anomalous parenthood controlled)

| Diagnosis of Child | Diagnosis of Parent (where anomalous parenthood) | |
|---|---|---|
| | Personality Disorder | Other Diagnosis |
| Mixed behaviour disorder | 9 (47·4%) | 5 (16·1%) |
| Other | 10 | 26 |
| Total | 19 | 31 |

(Critical ratio for difference between proportions = 2·408 p<0·02)

| | Diagnosis of Parent (where natural parenthood) | |
|---|---|---|
| | Personality Disorder | Other Diagnosis |
| Mixed behaviour disorder | 4 (20·0%) | 6 (9·0%) |
| Other | 16 | 61 |
| Total | 20 | 67 |

(Critical ratio not significant)

fact that within this group the disorders were more frequently severe and widespread. Numbers were too small to test whether the relationship of personality disorder to mixed behaviour disorder was merely an index of an association between parental personality disorder and severer disorders in the children, or whether personality disorder was related to the form of disorder in the child (i.e. disorders including both anti-social and neurotic symptoms).

TABLES 9.5 and 9.6 in the APPENDIX show that the distribution of symptoms and fields of disturbance in the child was very similar for all parental diagnostic groups and no difference reached statistical significance. The only difference that approached significance was the excess of children with disorders of school or of work among neurotic parents (p <0·09). This is noteworthy in view of Hersov's (1958) previous finding that children with the symptom of school refusal more often had neurotic parents than other children attending the clinic.

There were no statistically significant associations between the symptoms of the parental illness and either the fields of disturbance or the symptoms of the child's illness [TABLES 9.7 and 9.8 in the APPENDIX]. Although in a few cases the symptoms of parent and child were remarkably similar, this association did not occur more often than would be expected by chance. The only striking associations were when both parent and child had obsessional or hysterical symptoms, but the numbers were very small: 4 of the 11 children with obsessional symptoms were among the 9 whose parents also had obsessional symptoms, and 3 of the 5 children with hysterical symptoms were included in the 17 children of hysterical parents. Otherwise, particular types of psychiatric illness in the parent were not associated with particular types of disorder in the child.

Writers who have commented on similarities between the illnesses of parents and their children have usually referred to similar conflicts and psychopathological dynamics, rather than more formal characteristics. Similarities may exist, but would be difficult to test as interpretation of reactions would have to be measured instead of objective items of behaviour; it is possible of course that the symptoms of disorders in childhood are largely non-specific and that disorders should be grouped on the basis of other criteria. However, though it cannot be said that there is no relationship between the form of disorder in the parent and that in the child, no relationship, with the exceptions mentioned, was in fact found.

### Sex of the Parent who was ill
#### Mental illness

It has already been shown that mothers were more often ill than fathers, and that in a high proportion of cases both parents were ill. The further question arises: were aspects of the child's illness influenced by which parent was ill? The relationship between the sex of the mentally ill child and the sex of the mentally ill parent is shown in TABLE 9.9.

TABLE 9.9

RELATIONSHIP BETWEEN SEX OF PARENT WHO IS ILL AND SEX OF CHILD WHO IS ILL

| Sex of Child who is ill | Sex of Parent who is ill | | | Total |
| | Both ill | Father only ill | Mother only ill | |
| | No.　% | No.　% | No.　% | No. |
| Male | 20 (71·4) | 25 (67·6) | 37 (51·4) | 82 |
| Female | 8 (28·6) | 12 (32·4) | 35 (48·6) | 55 |
| Total | 28 | 37 | 72 | 137 |

The children of whom either the father alone was ill or of whom both parents were ill showed the usual 2 : 1 male preponderance, but among the children whose mother only was ill, the sexes were approximately equal. When the proportion of girls among the children of mentally ill mothers (48·6 per cent.) was compared with the proportion in the other two groups combined (30·8 per cent.) the difference was probably significant ($p < 0·04$). Thus, girls tended to have a *relatively* greater chance of psychiatric disorder when only the mother was mentally ill. The association was not present when the father was ill also.

## Physical Illness

No significant association was found between the sex of the parent who had a recurrent or chronic physical illness and the sex of the child who was mentally ill [TABLE 9.10 in the APPENDIX].

## Parental Death

The relationship between the sex of the deceased parent and the sex of the mentally ill child was examined [TABLE 9.11]. Although the groups overlapped considerably, it did appear that the mother's death and illness in the daughter were particularly associated. When the mother had died, half the mentally ill children were girls as compared with only a quarter (26·0 per cent.) when the father had died. This difference was significant ($p < 0·02$).

TABLE 9.11

RELATIONSHIP BETWEEN SEX OF DEAD PARENT AND SEX OF CHILD WHO IS ILL

| Sex of Child who is ill | Sex of dead parent | | | |
| | Both dead No. % | Father only dead No. % | Mother only dead No. % | Total No. |
|---|---|---|---|---|
| Male | 3 (75·0) | 37 (74·0) | 16 (50·0) | 56 |
| Female | 1 (25·0) | 13 (26·0) | 16 (50·0) | 30 |
| Total | 4 | 50 | 32 | 86 |

Thus, the sex of the mentally ill parent and of the deceased parent both bore a significant relationship to the sex of the child in the family who developed psychiatric disorder [demonstrated graphically in FIGURE 9.1]. The association was not found for parental physical illness. A similar association between death of the mother during childhood and psychiatric illness in the daughter was found by Barry and Lindemann (1960) in their study of adult neurotics, and Burt's (1925) data suggested a similar association with delinquency in girls although he did not comment on it. Apart from these studies the relationship between the sex of the dead or sick parent and the sex of the sick child has not received attention in the literature. Various writers, such as English and Pearson (1937), have commented on the greater harm to the child after the loss of the same-sexed parent but have not provided supporting data.

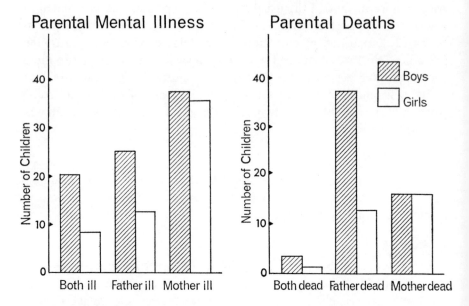

FIG. 9.1. (*a*) The relationship between the sex of the mentally ill parent and the sex of the child-patient.

(*b*) The relationship between the sex of the dead parent and the sex of the child-patient.

The sex of the mentally ill or dead parent did not influence the type of disorder in the child. Whichever parent was ill or deceased the disorder in the child was of the same duration, extent, severity, and diagnosis.

*Discussions and Conclusions*

The lack of correlation between the type of parental illness and the type of illness in the child argues against a specific genetic link between the disorders in parent and child, but one of the few significant findings was the relevance of which parent was mentally ill or had died. It was not that disorders only followed illness or death in the parent of one sex. There was a probably greater excess of mental illness among mothers than fathers but the higher rates of parental physical illness and death applied equally to both parents. Both parents were influential in the development of the children but there were differences according to which parent was affected. When psychiatric illness occurred in the *mother*, or when the mother died, there was a particular association with psychiatric disorder in the *daughter*, rather than the son. The association was significant, although not of a very high order, and suggested that in some way disorders in the children had a particular relationship with disorders in the same-sexed parent.

Apart from English and Pearson's (1937) speculative idea that loss of the same-sexed parent (by death) was more harmful to the child because it acted as an unexpected fulfilment of the child's death wishes towards the parent of the same sex, the association has been little discussed, but, the effects of parental absence on the aggressive fantasy of pre-school children, as shown in doll play, have been examined (Bach, 1946; Sears et al., 1946). Daughters were much less influenced by their father's absence than the sons, who showed a significant decrease in aggression. Lynn and Sawrey (1959) also found that father-absent boys, but not father-absent girls, showed poor peer adjustment in comparison with children from homes where the father was present.

The association between parental illness or death and psychiatric disorder in the same-sexed child needs also to be related to the evidence that differences in parental behaviour can be evaluated only with reference to the sex of the child (Brim, 1957; Bronfenbrenner, 1961). Parents tend to be more affectionate and lenient with a child of the opposite sex; more reserved and strict with one of their own sex (Becker, 1961; Becker et al., 1962; Brim, 1957; Bronfenbrenner, 1961). Parents also tend to interact more with the child of the same sex than the child of the opposite sex (Devereux et al., 1962). Such selective interactions between parents and children of the same sex are also reflected in statistical correlations between measures of child behaviour and ratings of parental practices and adjustment (Becker, 1961; Becker et al., 1962). Sex differences are most pronounced at lower educational levels and less evident in the upper social groupings. Thus, there is reason to think that parent-child relationships are, to some extent, 'sex-specific' although, as most of the investigations relied on questionnaire data, artifacts of response set have also to be considered (Bronfenbrenner, 1958).

Parental illness and death may be influential through effects on affectional and disciplinary relationships between parent and child which are, in part, 'sex-linked'. The effects of illness on parental attitudes and behaviour towards the child have not been studied, but deserve investigation. If a parent is dead, the child cannot experience relationships with a parent of that sex unless the surviving parent remarries. The parental psychiatric disorders which were particularly related to disorders in the children were mainly disorders of personality or chronic neurotic disorders in which disturbances of inter-personal relationships were often prominent.

Alternatively, the development of behaviour culturally appropriate to the child's sex may rely heavily upon a parental model, and when the model is absent through death or distorted by mental illness, the child's adjustment is likely to be unsatisfactory. This explanation has particular force in relation to parental death. The bereaved children who developed psychiatric disorder had generally lost their parent in early childhood but usually not until early adolescence did they first develop neurotic or behavioural abnormalities. A parental model of the same sex could be expected to be most important in adolescence, when responsible and adult-like behaviour is more consistently expected of the child. Whether or not this reliance on the parent of the same sex is a form of 'identification'—an ambiguous term (Bronfenbrenner, 1960) —the child's relationship with the parent of the same sex does seem to have particular importance. Research findings suggest that this especially close relationship with the same-sexed parent tends to be stronger in girls than boys (Rosenthal, 1962).

# CHAPTER X

# MODE OF INTERACTION BETWEEN ILLNESSES IN PARENTS AND THEIR CHILDREN

IN an earlier chapter, it was shown that children with psychiatric disorder were most often bereaved between the ages of two and five years but that psychiatric disorder was frequently not manifest until early adolescence. A few children developed symptoms within six months of the death of their parent, and their symptoms were more often like adult grief reactions. Frequently, however, symptoms were delayed several years and nearly a third of the children showed no signs of disorder until at least five years after the parental death. Disorder in the child seemed more often a reaction to the consequences of parental death than a direct result of grief.

The temporal relationship between parental physical and mental illness and psychiatric disorder in the child was examined but, although the time of onset of florid symptoms was known for the parents and usually for the children, easily defined episodes which could be related one to the other were rare. Many mental illnesses in parents developed against a background of lifelong deviance of personality; longstanding abnormalities of lesser degree often merged into the gradual onset of more florid symptoms. The question of recovery from the parental illness posed still greater problems. The disorder associated with abnormalities in the children were characteristically recurrent or chronic, and often symptoms were still present when the child attended hospital. However, from the age-distribution of the children at the time of onset of florid parental symptoms and from the significant preponderance of younger children at the time of attendance at hospital, it was evident that disorder in the child usually followed fairly soon after the parental illness, and in many cases a close temporal relationship had been recorded.

The temporal aspects of the interaction between psychiatric disorders in parents and their children could not be studied in detail as observations were entirely dependent upon comments in the records. Nevertheless, it often appeared that while the parent remained ill and the child remained at home, improvement rarely took place. This impression was supported by the large number of children for whom placement away from parents was recommended, usually after a clear demonstration that contact with the sick parent was deleterious for the child, usually borne out by improvement after removal from home, and sometimes relapse on return. Children and their parents often improved or deteriorated together. A few clearly improved and relapsed together. On the other hand, in one case an initial relationship was later lost when the mother remained ill and the child improved, and, in another case there was a marked lack of relationship between the state of the parent and that of the child. The temporal relationship between the illnesses of parents and their children often appeared closer in the younger children and least close in the adolescents, but there were exceptions. Although the child's illness appeared to follow the course of the parent's mental disorder in many (but not all) cases, the present study was not designed to examine the timing of these associations.

There were similar difficulties in measuring the temporal relationship between physical illnesses in the parent and psychiatric disorder in the child. The parental illnesses had all lasted at least a year (by definition) and had often run a chronic but fluctuating course over many years, with several periods of relapse, crisis, and remission. The clinic data were inadequate to relate the timing of these to the child's disorder, but suggested that only infrequently was there a long gap between the parental illness and the development of the child's disorder. Few showed the delayed onset common with bereavement, but there was also less frequently the close relationship that was seen with mental illness in the parent.

## Heredity or Environment?

Clearly, for any particular condition, the relative influence of heredity and environment can only be determined for any one situation, but the question is not a sterile one and has important implications, since analysis of the mode of interaction of genetic and non-genetic influences for any disorder may indicate ways in which the disorder may be prevented or treated.

Twin studies have an important place in the study of genetic factors. They present difficulties (Rutter *et al.*, 1963) and have limitations and biases (Jackson, 1960) but, nevertheless, they provide the best opportunity of examining the interaction of genetic and environmental influences (Slater, 1953). Shields (1954) in a study of 36 uniovular and 26 binovular twins among South London schoolchildren, found a greater concordance for child psychiatric disturbances among uniovular than among binovular twins. Complete concordance was found in none of the dizygotic pairs but was present in 36 per cent. of the monozygotic pairs; 69 per cent. of the dizygotic and 17 per cent. of the monozygotic were discordant. Other pairs were partially concordant. However, among the concordant pairs, twins showed similar symptoms in different contexts or at different times, so that qualitative concordance was greater than quantitative concordance. Environmental variables often appeared important. Shields concluded that genetic factors determined the physical basis of personality and that genetic effects on neurosis were through this influence on personality. Disorders not closely related to personality (e.g. juvenile delinquency) were less influenced by genetic factors than were disorders more closely related. The vulnerability was determined genetically but the disturbance was often precipitated by environmental circumstances.

This leaves open the question whether the genetic influences are those related to adult psychiatric disorder. Child disorders may be in part hereditary but still due to genes quite separate from those leading to any adult mental illness. Slater (1953), in his study of *Psychotic and Neurotic Illnesses in Twins*, found that in all diagnostic groups binovular, but not uniovular, twins showed a marked tendency for the more severely affected twin also to have been the more neurotic child. He argued that this association in binovular twins but not in uniovular twins (who were genetically indistinguishable) suggested a genetic determination, and that the constitutional make-up predisposing to mental illness in the adult helped to cause neurotic symptoms in childhood.

In the present study a number of children had both a natural parent and a step-parent, of whom one had had a psychiatric illness. It was thought that the contrast between the frequency of illness in the natural parent and that in the step-parent might help to disentangle genetic and environmental factors. However, illness referred to illness at any time, not just when the child attended hospital, which meant that there were two natural parents and (usually) only one step-parent to consider. As the rate of adult mental illness differs according to sex, the step-parent had to be compared with the natural parent of the same sex. Moreover, one natural parent had been with the child since birth (apart from temporary separations), whereas the step-parent came on the familial scene later, often much later, when the child was of an appreciable age. Therefore, the rate of illness in the step-parent had to be compared with the rate of illness in the natural parent that he or she had replaced, and it was necessary to equate (as far as was possible) the length of contact with the child. This left 17 cases. In one case, both the natural parent and the step-parent had had mental illness, in six cases the step-parent only, and in ten only the natural parent had had a psychiatric disorder. Thus, illness occurred in the step-parent almost as often as in the natural parent. The numbers are small, but suggest that genetic influences are probably not of major importance in the association between psychiatric disorders in parents and their children, though this should be accepted with caution in view of uncontrolled and possibly biasing factors which include: (*a*) in most cases the step-parent had been with the child for a shorter period than the natural parent he replaced; (*b*) the natural parent was not with the child at the time he attended hospital and so was sometimes not in contact with the child when he first developed symptoms; (*c*) the natural parent was with the child when he was younger (and data already presented suggest that this is the period of greatest susceptibility) whereas the step-parent began to have contact only when the child was older. As these biases work both for and against the hypothesis and probably balance out, the conclusion remains

H

that environmental factors are of considerable importance in the association between illnesses in parents and their children.[1]

This conclusion is also supported by circumstantial evidence from other parts of the investigation. Psychiatric disorder in the parent and child may have been associated through common genetic factors. On the other hand, death and chronic physical illness in the parent were also related to disorder in the child, and genetic factors will scarcely account in the same way for these associations. The effects of physical and mental illness showed some differences, but to the extent that they were similar, they provide indirect evidence that non-genetic factors may have been relevant in the association with mental illness, as well as with physical illness in the parent. The lack of relationship between the type of parental disorder and the type of disorder in the child argues strongly against a genetic link, as does the very hetero-geneity of disorders found in association with parental illness.

As there was nothing to suggest a sex-linked gene, the association between maternal illness or death and disorder in the daughter can best be explained in non-genetic terms. This also applies to the finding that psychiatric disorder in the mother was rather more likely to be associated with disorder in the child than was illness in the father. Stronger evidence in favour of an environmental effect was the finding that direct involvement of the child in the symptoms of the parental illness was more important than the form that the parental disorder took. In addition, in some cases the disorders in parent and child were related in time. This was reflected in the high rate of residential placement of these children, and in other instances the presence of a mentally ill parent was important in the *continuation* of the child's disorder whatever its cause.

Other writers have also placed the association firmly in terms of an environmental effect. The only exception is Campbell (1952) who, in respect of depressive illness, regarded the link as primarily genetic. Sometimes the direct effect of symptoms, such as murderous hostility to the child, has been examined (Anthony, 1959; Fabian and Donohue, 1956; Stern, 1948). Some writers have commented on how mothers may present their children's problems as their own symptoms (Gluck and Wrenn, 1959; Horn, 1954) or on the 'contagion' of symptoms (Ehrenwald, 1958). More frequently, the influence of the illness specifically upon the mother-child relationship (Huschka, 1941; Main, 1958; Treudley, 1946) or, more generally, upon

---

[1] If comparisons are made instead between the two parents with the child at the time of referral, illness occurred in the natural parent 12 times, in the step-parent 4 times and in both twice. On average the natural parent had been with the child over twice as long as the step-parent, so that there is a strong bias towards illness in the natural parent if the association is environmentally determined. Also of the 12 cases where the natural parent only was ill, this was the mother in all but one, because after divorce the child almost always remained with his mother. This causes a serious bias towards inflation of the rate of illness in natural parents because (a) adult psychiatric disorders occur more frequently in women, and (b) maternal mental disorder was, as has been shown, more likely to be associated with disorder in the child than was illness in the father. For these reasons it is thought that the comparison given in the main text is more valid.

interpersonal relationships within the home (Ackerman, 1958; Janet, 1925; Morris, 1958; Pollak, 1952) has received the chief emphasis. Janet (1925) noted that the association still occurred when the sick parent was a step-parent and that children who were raised away from the family circle sometimes escaped the affliction. Koch (1939) remarked that the disorders in parents and their children were frequently dissimilar. However, apart from these two writers, evidence bearing on the heredity/environment distinction was not presented.

The only other relevant data are provided by the O'Neal and Robins follow-up study (O'Neal et al., 1960). Former patients of a child guidance clinic had a high rate of adult psychiatric disease when compared with a matched control group. The most striking difference was the excess of adult sociopaths found among the antisocial and delinquent children. Many of the delinquents committed crimes in adult life. This argues for a continuity between child and adult antisocial disorders, and perhaps for a continuity between personality or psychopathic disorders in children and in adults. However, the proportion of neurotic adults who had been neurotic children (27 per cent.) was little different from the proportion in the control group (23 per cent.). The published findings of this study are based on as yet incomplete analyses, and the control group was rather small (35), but they suggest that the direct relationship between neurotic disorders of childhood and adult neurosis may be somewhat slender.

This issue has been discussed at some length because of its implications. The question of the relative importance of genetic and environmental factors in the association between mental illness in the adult and psychiatric disorder in the child cannot be regarded as settled. Most of the evidence is circumstantial and some is open to more than one interpretation. It is often easier to provide data which suggest an environmental effect than to prove a genetic basis. Even so, there is ample evidence to suggest that parental mental illness is often deleterious to the child through its environmental effects. That is not to say, of course, that factors intrinsic to the child are not important in the development of child psychiatric disorders. Indeed, the importance of temperamental differences (Rutter et al., 1964) and of genetic factors (Shields, 1954) in children's disorders have both been demonstrated. Genetic factors predisposing to mental illness in the adult may also play some part in the development of psychiatric disorders in childhood. Nevertheless, the association between parental illness and child psychiatric disorder is probably, in large part, environmentally determined. Parental illness is often associated with disturbances in the home and in the family and these contribute toward the development of the child's disorder.

# CHAPTER XI

# CONCLUSIONS

ALTHOUGH in the last few years there has been an increasing interest in the possibilities of prevention of mental disorders in children (see for example, Caplan, 1961, and van Krevelen, 1964), efforts have been hampered by lack of knowledge of the aetiology of child psychiatric disorder. In particular, few events could be identified as likely to lead to deviant behavioural development in the child. However, the strong association between parental illness and psychiatric disorder in the children suggests that parental illness may be such an event. We still know little about this association and statistical associations can never prove a causal relationship, but evidence (already discussed) suggests that the association is not fortuitous but represents the sometimes harmful consequences for the child of illness, especially chronic illness, in the parent. The extent of the risk to the children cannot be adequately assessed on the available evidence; prospective studies of families in which one parent is ill would be needed to determine this.

The effect is most striking with parental mental disorder but is also apparent with chronic physical illness. Parental death has also been shown to be related to the development of psychiatric disorder in the child, although the onset of the disorder seems more often to be delayed than when parental illness is involved. The children of mentally ill parents may have a genetically determined increased susceptibility to psychiatric disorder, but, as shown, this is unlikely to be the major factor in the association, or to be relevant to the association between parental physical illness or death and child psychiatric disorder. Instead, the disorder in the child must be viewed as one consequence of the impact of parental illness on the family, though the child's disorder also has an impact on family life, so that the interaction is two-way. Nevertheless, as parental illness usually precedes the development of the child's disorder it is appropriate to consider the parent-to-child effect as of prime importance.

Not all parental illnesses lead to deviant development in the children, nor, when there are harmful consequences, are all children equally affected. Children differ in their susceptibilities and more research is needed to determine which characteristics of the child are crucial in this respect. As with other 'stress' events boys appear more susceptible than girls and the younger child is more prone to disturbance than his older sibs. Temperamental characteristics, too, are important. They are related to the development of behaviour disorders in other situations (Rutter *et al.*, 1964) and are probably relevant also in the reaction of the child to parental illness.

Some characteristics of parental illness which suggest that disorder in the child may follow have been demonstrated, although most need further confirmation. The children are at risk for psychiatric disorder when parental physical illness becomes recurrent or chronic. Chronic illnesses are usually associated with disruption of family life and sometimes with financial hardship. In addition parents with chronic physical illness not infrequently show emotional disturbance sometimes amounting to frank mental illness. Other sick parents die, with further disruption of family life. Children bereaved in early childhood (but not infancy) seem most at risk, but frequently symptoms do not develop until adolescence some years later. The consequences of death rather than the death itself appear most important for the child's development. Children who lose a parent of the same sex are most likely to have psychiatric disorder, which suggests that the same-sexed parent plays a special role in the child's development—perhaps by providing a model for adult behaviour as the child reaches maturity. Discipline, too, especially of the older child, is often mainly carried out by the parent of the same sex. The child's emotional relationship with the same-sexed parent is often especially strong, particularly in girls.

Parental mental disorder is most likely to be followed by behavioural disturbance in the children when the parent exhibits long-standing abnormalities of personality. The 'seriousness' of the illness in terms of neurosis or psychosis is probably not important, but the involvement of the child in the symptoms of the parental illness does seem to be crucial. For example, delusions *per se* do not matter particularly but if the delusions directly involve the child and affect the parental care, it seems that the child is more likely to develop a psychiatric disorder. If the psychiatrist is to be on the alert for those disorders which are likely to have a harmful effect on other members of the family, he must inquire not only about the symptoms but also about the impact of the symptoms on other people. When the patient exhibited the symptom, where did he do it, who was present and what was the associated behaviour? If he was anxious was this accompanied by restrictions, impositions, etc., on other people in the home? If he was irritable, was this particularly directed against any one member of the family? Did he tend to 'pick on' any of the children? Were his obsessions accompanied by any forced alterations in the behaviour of others in the family? Was he violent? Did he express his suspicions or paranoid ideas to the children? Questions such as these are necessary in order to view the illness in its social context.

Children in families where *both* parents are ill or where the parental illness is accompanied by break-up of the marriage seem to be especially at risk. Continuing contact with a mentally sick parent might be very harmful for the child if the illness disrupts family life. On the other hand, contact with even a severely ill parent may still be beneficial, so long as the illness does not seriously impair affectional relationships within the home. Clearly, some illnesses are more socially disruptive than others, but the effect of illness on the health of other members of the family is probably related more to the impact on family life than to the clinical symptoms. Though the social disturbance associated with psychosis is well recognized, the disturbance accompanying chronic neurosis may be more severe, if less flamboyant, and the social consequences of chronic physical illness are often very similar, although possibly milder.

Though it is traditional in psychiatric practice to search for family attitudes or situations which may have influenced the development of the patient's disorder, it is less usual to dwell on the consequences for the family of the patient's illness. However, as parental illness often leads to distress and sometimes to psychiatric disorder in the spouse and children, more attention needs to be paid to the social effects. This is particularly important now that even severely disturbed patients are being increasingly treated as out-patients and the length of hospital stay has become progressively shorter (Brown, 1960).

The concern to avoid the deleterious effects of prolonged institutional care is healthy; in the past patients sometimes remained in hospital well past the time when it was beneficial for them. Severely ill patients can often be treated in the community, although the load on the family and on community resources may be considerable (see e.g. Pasamanick et al., 1964; Scarpitti et al., 1964).

What remains uncertain is the price that has to be paid for keeping the patient out of hospital in terms of the effect on the health of other members of the family. If the cost of keeping a parent in the community is the development of psychiatric disorder in the children then it may be too high.

A recent study of schizophrenics discharged from eight London mental hospitals showed that over half (57 per cent.) exhibited moderate symptoms on discharge and another one in six (17 per cent.) had severe symptoms (Wing et al., 1964). Over half the patients deteriorated in the year after discharge and 43 per cent. were readmitted to hospital. In three out of five families (59 per cent.) social relations within the patient's family became disturbed during this time—often to the limit of what would ordinarily be tolerable. In two out of five families (41 per cent.) an acute social crisis involved the police, neighbours or members of the general public, after severe family distress. The drugs prescribed were often not taken by the patients, and the general practitioners frequently complained of the lack of liaison with the mental hospital (Parkes et al., 1962). In spite of the marked social distress and disturbance, in only 2 per cent. of cases had a psychiatric social worker visited the home.

With a greater awareness of the family's plight and increased and improved community services, social disturbance could be considerably reduced. Day hospital care or temporary admission to a hostel catering for ambulant psychiatric patients may sometimes help to reduce the disturbance at home.

Other patients may be better going to work each day but returning to the hospital at night. In addition to psychotherapy and other psychiatric treatments directed to the improvement of disturbed family relationships, financial assistance, provision of a home help or other domestic services, advice to the family, occupational aid, patients' social groups, etc., may all play an important part in easing the family situation. Now that mentally ill patients, who in previous years would have been admitted to hospital, are being treated in the community, the liaison of family and hospital doctors with social services needs to be increasingly close. Well developed community services should reduce the burden on families. Nevertheless, in some cases the family distress will still be considerable and it may be better to admit the patient to relieve the situation at home. Doctors have a responsibility not only to their patients but also to the families of their patients.

Though the impact on families of mental illness in one member, and the family distress which often accompanies the care of a disturbed patient at home need emphasis, many psychiatric patients can be treated at home without any distress or disruption for the family. Normal family affection and family life may continue unimpaired in spite of severe mental disorder. What is required is that the doctors, social workers and others who have psychiatric patients under their care should be on the alert for the social consequences of illness and have the resources to help the family to cope with social crises and more longstanding social disturbances.

Though community care is undesirable when the load on the family becomes too great, admission to hospital should not be undertaken lightly. The remaining parent may need help with the children if the patient is admitted, or other arrangements for looking after the children may have to be considered. While the patient is in hospital, family adaptations take place, and on discharge the parent may return to a different family pattern. Both he and the family may require help to reorganize family life (Sampson et al., 1961 and 1962).

Much more study is required to measure the impact of psychiatric disorder on family life, (and also the effects of chronic physical illness, where family disorganisation may often be very similar (Ekdahl et al., 1962)). In particular the direct effect of mental symptoms on others in the home, e.g. through aggressive acts, restrictions due to morbid anxiety or fears, pathological neglect, or destructive behaviour, should be investigated. The family's perception of the patient's disorder may be important, as when they recognize the abnormal behaviour as due to illness, family adaptation may be easier. Many patients (especially neurotic patients) are ill for a long time before families make this recognition (Clausen, 1959b) especially when symptoms blend with the patient's previous personality and normal behaviour alternates with abnormal (Yarrow et al., 1955). The spouse and the children may be able to make allowances and adjustments when they perceive the patient's peculiar behaviour as due to illness. Such adjustments are more difficult when his irritability, moodiness, or hostility are seen as the normal feelings of a parent who has inexplicably turned against them.

It is important to determine how far chronic illness adversely affects affectional relationships within the home and how far a child's good relationship with the other parent can mitigate deleterious effects. Whether or not admission to hospital is disrupting may depend on the extent to which the admission has removed stress, and on the availability of family and community resources. The relationship between husband and wife and their roles in the home before the admission may affect the adjustment of the family at the time of illness, and the extent of contact with kin and neighbours may determine whether help is available and used (Bott, 1957; Sampson et al., 1962). We need also to know more about the stresses imposed by longstanding illnesses which lead to divorce or separation and the consequences of this for the children. Children may be adversely affected by disturbed relationships between the two parents. Mental disorder, especially longstanding mental disorder, is often associated with hostility and discord between husband and wife. Quarrelling and bickering may increase and the atmosphere in the home may reflect rising tension. This may sometimes have more impact on the child than the mental illness itself.

Illness may cause economic difficulties through loss of job or reduced earning capacity, especially when admission to hospital is required or when the illness is chronic or recurrent. The extent of financial hardship in mental disorder or chronic physical illness, and its effect on the family are not yet known. The spouse may have to go out to work, extra responsibilities may fall on the children or they may have to stay away from school to look after the sick parent.

Clausen's findings (1959b) suggested that even in severe mental illness the mother's physical care of the children often remained adequate for a long while, though illness sometimes led her to neglect her home and children. In his sample of schizophrenics admitted to hospital the daily family routine was usually markedly disrupted during the month before admission. *Distortion* of the emotional and social aspects of child care may be more common, especially among parents with personality disorders or chronic neurotic conditions, and psychiatric disorder may become associated with abnormalities in family social and recreational life. Clearly, much remains to be known but enough is known to suggest that detailed attention should be paid routinely to the impact of psychiatric or chronic physical illness on the family. Children in these families should be regarded as at risk, as they should also when a parent dies. Many children in such families will develop normally but others may develop disorders which might have been prevented.

Attention in this chapter has largely been confined to the issues as they face those caring for adult patients, but the high rate of frank mental disorder in the parents of children attending psychiatric clinics also has important implications for the child psychiatrist. The child psychiatrist should have a thorough grounding in adult psychiatry so that he is fully aware of the nature and treatment of the illnesses he encounters in the parents of his patients, whether he treats the parent himself or whether another psychiatrist does so. In either case, the care of the parent is likely to have an important bearing on the care of the child. Close liaison between psychiatrists treating adults and those treating children is also necessary.

Because of the frequent pathology among parents, some have suggested that child psychiatry should become 'family psychiatry' (Ackerman, 1958; Howells, 1963). In so far as this means that child psychiatrists must be aware that a child's disorder may reflect disorder in other members of the family this is a healthy trend. But similar issues apply in all branches of psychiatry so that 'family psychiatry' is in no way confined to those looking after children. It is too narrow in that child psychiatrists need to be aware not only of the effects of psychiatric disorder in other members of the family but also of *physical* disorder and its social consequences. It is wrong if it implies that if there is a deviant child there must also be a deviant parent. Some disorders in children stem essentially from abnormalities intrinsic to the child and treatment of the parents would be superfluous. 'Family psychiatry' like 'psychosomatic medicine' should represent an approach shared by all psychiatrists rather than be a speciality of its own. Nevertheless, the importance of interaction between illnesses in different members of the same family necessitates that psychiatry in all its branches should incorporate what is valuable in this approach.

# REFERENCES

ABRAHAM, K. (1911) Notes on the psycho-analytical investigation and treatment of manic-depressive insanity and allied conditions, *Selected Papers of Karl Abraham* (1949), London.

ABRAHAMSON, J. H. (1960) The complaints of mothers and their daughters, *S. Afr. T. Geneesk.*, **34**, 681.

ACKERMAN, N. W. (1956a) Interlocking pathology in family relationships, *Changing Concepts of Psychoanalytic Medicine*, p. 35, New York.

—— (1956b) Disturbances of mothering and criteria for treatment, *Amer. J. Orthopsychiat.*, **26**, 252.

—— (1958) Towards an integrative therapy of the family, *Amer. J. Psychiat.*, **114**, 727.

ACKERMAN, N. W., and BEHRENS, M. L. (1956) A study in family diagnosis, *Amer. J. Orthopsychiat.*, **26**, 66.

AINSWORTH, M. D. (1962) The effects of maternal deprivation: a review of findings and controversy in the context of research strategy, *Deprivation of Maternal Care: a Reassessment of its Effects*, Public Health Paper No. 14, Geneva: W.H.O.

ANASTASI, A. (1954) *Psychological Testing*, New York.

ANTHONY, E. J. (1959) A group of murderous mothers, *Acta psychother.*, **7**, Suppl. 1–6.

ANTHONY, S. (1940) *The Child's Discovery of Death*, London.

APLEY, J. (1963) Family patterning and childhood disorder, *Lancet*, **i**, 67.

ARNAUD, S. H. (1959) Some psychological characteristics of children of multiple sclerotics, *Psychosom. Med.*, **21**, 8.

ARTHUR, B., and KEMME, M. L. (1964) Bereavement in childhood, *J. child Psychol. Psychiat.*, **5**, 37.

BACH, G. R. (1946) Father-fantasies and father-typing in father-separated children, *Child Development*, **17**, 63.

BAKER, A. A., MORISON, M., GAME, J. A., and THORPE, J. G. (1961) Admitting schizophrenic mothers with their babies, *Lancet*, **ii**, 237.

BANISTER, H., and RAVDEN, M. (1944) The problem child and his environment, *Brit. J. Psychol.*, **34**, 60.

—— (1945) ibid., **35**, 82.

BARKER, R. G. in collaboration with WRIGHT, B. A., MEYERSON, L., and GONICK, M. R. (1953) *Adjustment to physical handicap and illness: A survey of the Social Psychology of Physique and Disability*, Social Science Research Council Bulletin No. 55

BARRY, H. (1949) Significance of maternal bereavement before the age of eight in psychiatric patients, *Arch. Neurol. Psychiat.*, **62**, 630.

BARRY, H., and BOUSFIELD, W. A. (1937) Incidence of orphanhood among fifteen hundred psychotic patients, *J. genet. Psychol.*, **50**, 198.

BARRY, H., and LINDEMANN, E. (1960) Critical ages for maternal bereavement in psychoneuroses, *Psychosom. Med.*, **22**, 166.

BECKER, W. C. (1961) Unpublished supplemental analyses of parent-child data.

BECKER, W. C., PETERSON, D. B., LURIA, Z., SHOEMAKER, D. J., and HELLMER, L. A. (1962) Relations of factors derived from parent interview ratings to behaviour problems of five-year-olds, *Child Development*, **33**, 509.

BELL, J. E. (1962) Recent advances in family group therapy, *J. child Psychol. Psychiat.*, **1**, 1.

BENNETT, I. (1960) *Delinquent and Neurotic Children*, London.

BERKSON, J. (1946) Limitations of the application of four-fold table analysis to hospital data, *Biometrics*, **2**, 264.

BETHELL, M. F. (1958) Restriction and habits in children, *Zschr. Kinder psychiat. (Basel)*, **25**, 264.

BLACKER, C. P. (1958) Disruption of Marriage, *Lancet*, **i**, 578.

BLOMFIELD, J. M., and DOUGLAS, J. W. B. (1956) Bedwetting: prevalence among children aged 4 to 7 years, *Lancet*, **i**, 850.

BLUMBERG, E. M., WEST, P. M., and ELLIS, F. W. (1954) A possible relationship between psychological factors and human cancer, *Psychosom. Med.*, **14**, 237.

BOTT, E. (1957) *Family and Social Network*, London.

BOWLBY, J. (1946) *Forty-four Juvenile Thieves*, London.

—— (1952) *Maternal Care and Mental Health*, Geneva, W.H.O. Monograph No. 2.

—— (1953) Some pathological processes set in train by early mother-child separation, *J. ment. Sci.*, **99**, 265.

—— (1960) Grief and mourning in infancy and early childhood, *Psychoanal. Study Child*, **15**, 9.

—— (1961a) Childhood mourning and its implications for psychiatry, *Amer. J. Psychiat.*, **118**, 481.

—— (1961b) Processes of mourning, *Int. J. Psychoanalysis*, **42**, 317.

BOWLBY, J., AINSWORTH, M., BOSTON, B., and ROSENBLUTH, D. (1956) The effects of mother-child separation: A follow-up study, *Brit. J. med. Psychol.*, **29**, 211.

BRIDGER, W. (1962) Ethological concepts and human development, in *Recent Advances in Biological Psychiatry* (Ed. Wortis J.), New York, 95–107.

BRIM, O. G. (1957) The parent-child relation as a social system: I. Parent and Child roles, *Child Development*, **28**, 343.

BRODMAN, K., MITTELMAN, B., WECHSLER, D., WEIDER, A., and WOLFF, H. G. (1947) The relation of personality disturbances to duration of convalescence for acute respiratory infections, *Psychosom. Med.*, **9**, 37.

BRONFENBRENNER, U. (1958) Socialization and social class through time and space, *Readings in Social Psychology*. (Ed. Maccoby, E., Newcomb, T. M., and Hartley, E. L.), pp. 400–25, New York.

—— (1960) Freudian theories of identification and their derivatives, *Child Development*, **31**, 15.

—— (1961) Towards a theoretical model for the analysis of parent-child relationships in a social context, *Parental Attitudes and Child Behaviour* (Ed. J. C. Glidewell), pp. 90–109, Springfield, Ill.

BROOKE, E. (1960) Contribution to discussion on 'A comparative study of psychiatric classifications', *Proc. roy. Soc. Med.*, **53**, 128.

—— (1961) Personal communication.

BROWN, F. (1961) Depression and Childhood bereavement, *J. ment. Sci.*, **107**, 754.

BROWN, G. W. (1960) Length of hospital stay and schizophrenia: a review of statistical studies, *Acta psychiat. neurol. scand.*, **35**, 414.

—— (1965) Personal communication.

BROWN, G. W., PARKES, C. M., and WING, J. K. (1961) Admissions and readmissions to three London mental hospitals, *J. ment. Sci.*, **107**, 1070.

BUCK, C., and LAUGHTON, K. (1959) Family patterns of illness: the effect of psychoneurosis in the parent upon illness in the child, *Acta psych. neurol. scand.*, **34**, 165.

BURLINGHAM, D., and FREUD, A. (1942) *Young Children in Wartime*, London.
—— (1944) *Infants without Families*, London.
BURT, C. (1925) *The Young Delinquent*, London.
BURT, C., and HOWARD, M. (1952) The nature and causes of maladjustment among children of school age, *Brit. J. Psychol. (Statistical Section)*, **5**, 39.
CAMERON, K. (1955) Diagnostic categories in child psychiatry, *Brit. J. med. Psychol.*, **28**, 67.
CAMPBELL, J. D. (1952) Manic-depressive psychosis in children, *J. nerv. ment. Dis.*, **116**, 424.
CANAVAN, M. M., and CLARK, R. (1923a). The mental health of 463 children from dementia praecox stock (1), *Mental Hygiene*, **7**, 137.
—— (1923b) The mental health of 581 offspring of non-psychotic parents, *Mental Hygiene*, **7**, 770.
—— (1936) The mental health of 463 children from dementia praecox stock (2), *Mental Hygiene*, **20**, 463.
CAPLAN, G. (1961) *Prevention of Mental Disorders in Children*, New York.
CASLER, L. (1961) Maternal deprivation: A critical review of the literature, *Monograph Soc. Res. child Dev.*, **26**, No. 2.
CHESS, S., THOMAS, A., BIRCH, H. G., and HERTZIG, M. (1960) Implications of a longitudinal study of child development for child psychiatry, *Amer. J. Psychiat.*, **117**, 434.
CHESS, S., THOMAS, A., RUTTER, M., and BIRCH, H. G. (1963) Interaction of temperament and environment in the production of behavioural disturbances in children, *Amer. J. Psychiat.*, **120**, 142.
CIOCCO, A., DENSEN, P. M., and THOMPSON, D. J. (1954) On the association between health and social problems in the population, *Milbank Mem. Fund Quart.*, **32**, 247.
CLAUSEN, J. A. (1959a) The sociology of mental illness, in *Sociology Today: Problems and Prospects* (Eds. Merton, R. K., Broom, L., and Cottrell, J. S.), p. 485, New York.
—— (1959b) The marital relationship antecedent to hospitalization of a spouse for mental illness, Unpublished paper.
CLAUSEN, J. A., and YARROW, M. R. (1955) Paths to the mental hospital, *J. social Issues*, **11**, 25.
CLEIN, L. J. (1959) *Non-attenders at a children's clinic*, D.P.M. Dissertation, London.
CLEVELAND, E. J., and LONGAKER, W. D. (1957) Neurotic patterns in the family, *Explorations in Social Psychiatry* (Eds. Leighton, A. H., Clausen, J. A., and Wilson, R. N.), p. 167, London.
CLOW, J. M. (1961) Personal communication.
COWIE, V. (1961a) Children of psychotics—a controlled study, *Proc. roy. Soc. Med.*, **54**, 675.
—— (1961b) The incidence of neurosis in the children of psychotics, *Acta psych. scand.*, **37**, 1.
CRAIG, W. S. (1956) The child in the maladjusted household, *Practitioner*, **177**, 21.
CUMMINGS, J. D. (1944) The incidence of emotional symptoms in school children, *Brit. J. educ. Psychol*, **14**, 151.
—— (1946) ibid., **16**, 163.
CYTRYN, L., GILBERT, A., and EISENBERG, L. (1960) The effectiveness of tranquillizing drugs plus supportive psychotherapy in treating behaviour disorders of children: a double-blind study of eighty out-patients, *Amer. J. Orthopsychiat.*, **30**, 113.

DE LA MATA, R. C., GINGRAS, C., and WITTKOWER, E. D. (1960) Impact of sudden, severe disablement of the father upon the family, *Canad. med. Assoc. J.*, **82,** 1015.

DEUTSCH, H. (1937) Absence of grief, *Psychoanalyt. Quart.*, **6,** 12.

DEVEREUX, E. C., BRONFENBRENNER, U., and SUCI, G. J. (1962) Patterns of parent behaviour in America and West Germany, A cross-national comparison, To be published.

DONIGER, C. B. (1962) Children whose mothers are in a mental hospital, *J. child Psychol. Psychiat.*, **3,** 165.

DOUGLAS, J. W. B. (1961) Personal communication.

DOUGLAS, J. W. B., and BLOMFIELD, J. M. (1958) *Children under Five*, London.

DOUST, J. W. L. (1952) Psychiatric aspects of somatic immunity: differential incidence of physical disease in the histories of psychiatric patients, *Brit. J. soc. Med.*, **6,** 49.

DOWNES, J. (1942) Illness in the chronic disease family, *Amer. J public Health*, **32,** 589.

—— (1945) Sickness as an index of the need for health supervision of the school child, *Amer. J. public Health*, **35,** 593.

—— (1950) Cause of illness among males and females, *Milbank Mem. Fund Quart.*, **28,** 407.

—— (1951) Method of statistical analysis of chronic disease in a longitudinal study of illness, *Milbank Mem. Fund Quart.*, **29,** 404.

—— (1952) The longitudinal study of families as a method of research, *Milbank Mem. Fund Quart.*, **30,** 101.

DOWNES, J., and SIMON, K. (1953) Psychoneurotic patients and their families, *Psychosom. Med.*, **15,** 463.

—— (1954) Characteristics of psycho-neurotic patients and their families as revealed in a general morbidity survey, *Milbank Mem. Fund Quart.*, **32,** 42.

DREIKURS, R. (1951) Family group therapy in the Chicago Community Child Guidance Center, *Mental Hygiene*, **35,** 291.

EARLE, A. M., and EARLE, B. V. (1961) Early maternal deprivation and later psychiatric illness, *Amer. J. Orthopsychiat.*, **31,** 181.

EDELSTON, H. (1943) Separation anxiety in young children: a study of hospital cases, *Genet. Psychol. Monogr.*, **28,** 3.

EHRENWALD, J. (1958) Neurotic interaction and patterns of pseudo-heredity in the family, *Amer. J. Psychiat.*, **115,** 134.

—— (1963) *Neurosis in the Family and Patterns of Psychological Defence*, New York.

EISENBERG, L. (1960) The challenge of change, *Child Welfare*, April 1960.

EKDAHL, M. C., RICE, E. P., and SCHMIDT, W. M. (1962) Children of parents hospitalized for mental illness, *Amer. J. public Health*, **52,** 428.

ELLES, G. W. (1961) Collateral treatment in a family by psychoanalytic techniques, *Brit. J. psychiat. soc. Work*, **16,** 3.

ENGLISH, O. S., and PEARSON, G. H. J. (1937) *Common Neuroses of Children and Adults*, London.

EWEN, S. J. (1952) Psychiatric aspects of dentistry: in *Psychology of Physical Illness* (Ed. Bellak, L.), London.

FABIAN, A. A., and DONOHUE, J. F. (1956) Maternal depression: a challenging child guidance problem, *Amer. J. Orthopsychiat.*, **26,** 400.

FENICHEL, O. (1945) *The Psychoanalytic Theory of Neuroses*, pp. 393–6, New York.

FERGUSON, T., and MACPHAIL, A. M. (1954) *Hospital and Community*, London.

FISHER, M., and MENDELL, D. (1956) The communication of neurotic patterns over two and three generations, *Psychiatry*, **19,** 41.

FOLSOM, J. K. (1934) *The Family: Its Sociology and Social Psychiatry*, New York.

FOULKES, S. H., and ANTHONY, E. J. (1957) *Group Psychotherapy. The Psychoanalytic Approach*, London.

FREUD, S. (1917) Mourning and Melancholia: in *Collected Papers, Vol. IV*, London.

GARDNER, G. E. (1956) Separation of the parents and the emotional life of the child, *Mental Hygiene*, **40**, 53.

GARDNER, N. H. (1949) The later adjustment of children born in mental hospital to psychotic mothers, *Smith Coll. Stud. soc. Work*, **19**, 137 (abstract of thesis).

GERARD, D. L., and SIEGEL, J. (1950) The family background of schizophrenia, *Psychiat. Quart.*, **24**, 47.

GESELL, A., and ILG, F. L. (1946) *The Child from Five to Ten*, New York.

GLUCK, I., and WRENN, M. (1959) Contribution to the understanding of disturbances of mothering, *Brit. J. med. Psychol.*, **32**, 171.

GLUECK, S., and GLUECK, E. (1950) *Unravelling Juvenile Delinquency*, New York.

GOLDFARB, W. (1943) Infant rearing and problem behaviour, *Amer. J. Orthopsychiat.*, **13**, 249.

GOODENOUGH, F. L., and LEAHY, A. M. (1927) The effect of certain family relationships upon the development of personality, *J. genet. Psychol.*, **34**, 45.

GRAD, J., and SAINSBURY, P. (1963) Mental illness and the family, *Lancet*, **i**, 544.

GREENFIELD, N. S., ROESSLER, R., and CROSLEY, A. (1959). Ego strength and length of recovery from infectious mononucleosis, *J. nerv. ment. Dis.*, **128**, 125.

GREER, S. (1964) The relationship between parental loss and attempted suicide, *Brit. J. Psychiat.*, **110**, 698.

GREGORY, I. (1958) Studies of parental deprivation in psychiatric patients, *Amer. J. Psychiat.*, **115**, 432.

—— (1959) Husband and wives admitted to mental hospital, *J. ment. Sci.*, **105**, 457.

GRUENBERG, E. M., and BELLIN, S. S. (1957) The impact of mental disease on society, *Explorations in Social Psychiatry* (Eds. Leighton, A. H., Clausen, J. A., and Wilson, R. N.), p. 341, London.

GRUNBERG, F., and POND, D. A. (1957) Conduct disorders in epileptic children, *J. Neurol. Neurosurg. Psychiat.*, **20**, 65.

GRUNEBAUM, H. U., WEISS, J. L. HIRSCH, L. L., and BARRETT, J. E. (1963a) The baby on the ward, *Psychiatry*, **26**, 39.

GRUNEBAUM, H. U., and WEISS, J. L. (1963b) Psychotic mothers and their children: joint admission to an adult psychiatric hospital, *Amer. J. Psychiat.*, **119**, 927.

HANVIK, L. J., and BYRUM, M. (1959) M.M.P.I. profiles of parents of child psychiatric patients, *J. clin. Psychol.*, **15**, 427.

HARE, E. H. (Ed.) (1959) *The Bethlem Royal Hospital and The Maudsley Hospital: Triennial Statistical Report*, Years 1955-7.

HARE, E. H., and SHAW, G. K. (1965) A study in family health: (2) a comparison of the health of fathers, mothers and children, *Brit. J. Psychiat.*, **111**, 467.

HARLOW, H. F. (1958) The nature of love, *Amer. Psychologist*, **13**, 673.

—— (1960) Primary affectional patterns in primates, *Amer. J. Orthopsychiat.*, **30**, 676.

—— (1961) The development of affectional patterns in infant monkeys, *Determinants of Infant Behaviour*, (Ed. Foss, B. M.), London.

HARLOW, H. F., and ZIMMERMANN, R. R. (1959) Affectional responses in the infant monkey, *Science*, **130**, 421.

HEILPERN, E. P. (1943) Psychological problems of stepchildren, *Psychoanalyt. Rev.*, **30**, 163.

HEINICKE, C. M. (1956) Some effects of separating two-year-old children from their parents: a comparative study, *Human Relations*, **9**, 105.

HERSOV, L. (1958) *A psychiatric study of school refusal*, M.D. Thesis, Witwatersand.

HERSOV, L. A. (1960a) Persistent non-attendance at school, *J. child Psychol. Psychiat.*, **1**, 130.

—— (1960b) Refusal to go to school, ibid., **1**, 137.

HEWITT, L. E., and JENKINS, R. L. (1946) *Fundamental Patterns of Maladjustment —the Dynamics of their Origin*, Springfield, Ill.

HILGARD, J. R., and NEWMAN, M. R. (1959) Anniversaries in mental illness, *Psychiatry*, **22**, 113.

HILGARD, J. R., NEWMAN, M. F., and FISH, F. (1960) Strength of adult ego following childhood bereavement, *Amer. J. Orthopsychiat.*, **30**, 788.

HILL, R. (1949) *Families Under Stress*, London.

HINDE, R. A., THORPE, W. H., and VINCE, M. A. (1956) The following response of young coots and moorhens, *Behaviour*, **9**, 214.

HINKLE, L. E. (1959) Physical health, mental health and the social environment: some characteristics of healthy and unhealthy people: in *Recent Contributions of Biological and Psychosocial Investigations to Preventive Psychiatry*, (Ed. Ojemann, R. H.), Iowa City, Iowa.

HINKLE, L. E., and WOLFF, H. G. (1957) The nature of man's adaptation to his total environment and the relation of this to illness, *Arch. int. Med.*, **99**, 442.

HINTON, J. M. (1963) The physical and mental distress of dying, *Quart. J. Med.*, **32**, 1.

HIRSCH, N. D. N. (1937) *Dynamic Causes of Juvenile Crime*, Cambridge, Mass.

HOLMAN, P. (1953) Some factors in the aetiology of maladjustment in children, *J. ment. Sci.*, **99**, 654.

HOLMES, T. H., JOFFE, J. R., KETCHAM, J. W., and SHEEHY, T. F. (1961), Experimental study of prognosis, *J. psychosom. Res.*, **5**, 238.

HOPKINS, P. (1959) Health and happiness and the family, *Brit. J. clin. Practice*, **13**, 311.

HORN, M. L. V. (1954) Parental identification of the child-patient with a psychotic relative, *Smith Coll. Stud. soc. Work*, **25**, 29.

HOWELLS, J. G., (1962) The nuclear family as the functional unit in psychiatry, *J. ment. Sci.*, **108**, 675.

—— (1963) *Family Psychiatry*, Edinburgh.

HOWELLS, J. G., and LAYNG, J. (1955) Separation experiences and mental health: a statistical study, *Lancet*, **ii**, 285.

HUSCHKA, M. (1941) Psychopathological disorders in the mother, *J. nerv. ment. Dis.*, **94**, 76.

ILLINGWORTH, R. S., and HOLT, K. S. (1955) Children in hospital: some observations on their reactions with special reference to daily visiting, *Lancet*, **ii**, 1257.

INGHAM, H. V. (1949) A statistical study of family relationships and psychoneurosis, *Amer. J. Psychiat.*, **106**, 91.

IRVINE, E. E. (1961) Psychosis in parents: mental illness as a problem for the family, *Brit. J. psychiat. soc. Work*, **6**, 21.

JACKSON, D. D. (1960) A critique of the literature on the genetics of schizophrenia, *The Etiology of Schizophrenia* (Ed. Jackson, D. D.), pp. 37–90, New York.

JANET, P. (1925) *Psychological Healing*, Vol. 1 (trans. by Paul, E. and C.), pp. 426–7, London.

KANNER, L. (1944) Behaviour disorders in childhood: in *Personality and the Behaviour Disorders* (Ed. Hunt, J. McV.), New York.

—— (1959) The thirty-third Maudsley lecture: Trends in Child Psychiatry, *J. ment. Sci.*, **105**, 581.

KELLNER, R. (1963) *Family Ill Health*, London.

KLEIN, M. (1934) A contribution to the psychogenesis of manic-depressive states, *Contributions to Psychoanalysis, 1921–45*, London (1948).

KLOPFER, B. (1957) Psychological variables in human cancer, *J. proj. Techn.*, **21**, 329.

KOCH, A. (1939) Nevrose dos paes, nevrose dos filhos, *Neurobiologia*, **2**, 320.

KRASNOFF, A. (1959) Psychological variables and human cancer: a cross-validation study, *Psychosom. Med.*, **21**, 291.

KREITMAN, N. (1962) Mental disorder in married couples, *J. ment. Sci.*, **108**, 438.

—— (1964) The patient's spouse, *Brit. J. Psychiat.*, **110**, 159.

LANE, M. (1956) The effect of leucotomy on family life, *Brit. J. psych. soc. Work*, **3**, 18.

LAPOUSE, R., and MONK, M. A. (1958) An epidemiologic study of behaviour characteristics in children, *Amer. J. publ. Health*, **48**, 1134.

—— (1959) Fears and worries in a representative sample of children, *Amer. J. Orthopsychiat.*, **29**, 803.

LAUTERBACH, C., LONDON, P., and BRYAN, J. (1961) M.M.P.I.'s of parents of Child Guidance cases, *J clin. Psychol.*, **17**, 151.

LEHRMAN, D. S. (1953) A critique of Konrad Lorenz's theory of instinctive behaviour, *Quart. Rev. Biol.*, **28**, 337.

LEWIS, A. J. (1956) Social Psychiatry, *Lectures on the Scientific Basis of Medicine*, *VI, 1956–7*, p. 116, London.

—— (1957) The offspring of parents both mentally ill, *Acta genet.*, **7**, 349.

LEWIS, H. (1954) *Deprived Children*, London.

LINDEMANN, E. (1944) Symptomatology and Management of Acute Grief, *Amer. J. Psychiat.*, **101**, 141.

LITAUER, W. (1957) *Juvenile Delinquents in a Psychiatric Clinic*, London.

LONGAKER, W. D., and GODDEN, J. O. (1960) A comparison of organic and psychiatric symptoms in a small town, *Acta psych. neurol. scand.*, **35**, 91.

LOWREY, L. G. (1940) Personality distortion and early institutional care, *Amer. J. Orthopsychiat.*, **10**, 576.

LUDY, J. (1939) Social adjustment of children of psychotic mothers, *Smith Coll. Stud. soc. Work*, **10**, 148.

LYNN, D. B., and SAWREY, W. L. (1959) The effects of father-absence on Norwegian boys and girls, *J. abn. soc. Psychol.*, **59**, 258.

MAAS, H. S. (1955) Socio-cultural factors in psychiatric clinic services for children, *Smith Coll. Stud. soc. Work*, **25**, 1.

McCORD, W., and McCORD, J., with ZOLA, I. K. (1959) *Origins of Crime*, New York.

MACDONALD, M. (1939) The social adjustment of children of psychoneurotic mothers, *Smith Coll. Stud. soc. Work*, **10**, 148 (abstract of thesis).

MAIN, T. F. (1958) Mothers with children in a psychiatric hospital, *Lancet*, **ii**, 845.

MARKS, P. A. (1961) An assessment of the diagnostic process in a child guidance clinic, *Psychol. Monogr.*, **75**, 1.

MARRIS, P. (1958) *Widows and their Families*, London.

MILLER, F. J. W., COURT, S. D. M., WALTON, W. S., and KNOX, E. G. (1960), *Growing up in Newcastle upon Tyne*, London.

MILLS, E. (1962) *Living with Mental Illness*, London.

MINISTRY OF EDUCATION (1955) *Report of the Committee on Maladjusted Children*, London.

MOLTZ, H. (1960) Imprinting: empirical basis and theoretical significance, *Psychol. Bull.*, **57**, 291.

MOORE, T. W. (1963) Chap. VI. Effects on the children, *Working Mothers and Their Children* (Yudkin, S. and Holme, A.), London.

MORRIS, D. P., SOROKER, E., and BURRUSS, G. (1954) Follow-up studies of shy, withdrawn children—I. Evaluation of later adjustment, *Amer. J. Orthopsychiat.*, **24**, 743.

MORRIS, H. H., ESCOLL, P. J., and WEXLER, R. (1956) Aggressive behaviour disorders of childhood—a follow-up study, *Amer. J. Psychiat.*, **112**, 991,

MORRIS, P. (1958) Some disturbances of family functioning associated with psychiatric illness, *Brit. J. med. Psychol.*, **31**, 104.

MORRIS, W. W., and NICHOLAS, A. L. (1950) Intra-familial personality configurations among children with primary behaviour disorders and their parents: a Rorschach investigation, *J. clin. Psychol.*, **6**, 309.

MURRAY, H. A. (1937) Visceral manifestations of personality, *J. abnorm. soc. Psychol.*, **32**, 161.

NAGY, M. (1948) The child's theories concerning death, *J. genet. Psychol.*, **73**, 3.

NEUBAUER, P. B. (1960) The one-parent child and his Oedipal development, *Psychoanalyt. Stud. Child*, **15**, 286.

NIELSON, J. (1964) Mental disorders in married couples (assortative mating), *Brit. J. Psychiat.*, **110**, 683.

NORRIS, V. (1956) A statistical study of the influence of marriage on the hospital care of the mentally sick, *J. ment. Sci.*, **102**, 467.

NORRIS, V. (1959) *Mental Illness in London*, Maudsley Monograph No. 6, London.

NORTON, A. (1952) Incidence of neurosis related to maternal age and birth order, *Brit. J. soc. Med.*, **6**, 253.

O'CONNOR, N. (1956) The evidence for the permanently disturbing effects of mother-child separation, *Acta psychologica*, **12**, 174.

O'CONNOR, N., and FRANKS, C. (1960) Childhood upbringing and other environmental factors, *Handbook of Abnormal Psychology* (Ed. Eysenck, H. J.), London.

OLTMAN, J. E., McGARRY, J. J., and FRIEDMAN, S. (1952), Parental deprivation and the 'broken home' in dementia praecox and other mental disorders, *Amer. J. Psychiat.*, **108**, 685.

O'NEAL, P., and ROBINS, L. N. (1958) The relation of childhood behaviour problems to adult psychiatric status: A 30-year follow-up study of 150 subjects, *Amer. J. Psychiat.*, **114**, 961.

—— (1959) Childhood patterns predictive of adult schizophrenia: a 30-year follow-up study, *Amer. J. Psychiat.*, **115**, 385.

O'NEAL, P., BERGMAN, J., SCHAFER, J., and ROBINS, L. N. (1960) The relation of childhood behaviour problems to adult psychiatric status, *Amer. Psychiat. Ass. District Branches Publ. I, Scientific Papers and Discussions*, p. 99.

OSWALD, I. (1958) Deprivation of parents during childhood, its frequency in some contemporary young servicemen, *Brit. med. J.*, **i**, 1515.

PARKES, C. M. (1962) *Reactions to Bereavement*, M.D. Thesis, Univ. of London.

—— (1964) Recent bereavement as a cause of mental illness, *Brit. J. Psychiat.*, **110**, 465.

PARKES, C. M., BROWN, G. W., and MONCK, E. M. (1962) The general practitioner and the schizophrenic patient, *Brit. med. J.*, **i**, 972.

PARSONS, T., and BALES, R. F. (1955) *Family, Socialization and Interaction Process*, Glencoe, Illinois.

PASAMANICK, B., SCARPITTI, F. R., LEFTON, M., DINITZ, S., WEINERT, J. J., and McPHEETERS, H. (1964) Home vs hospital care for schizophrenics, *J. Amer. med. Ass.*, **187**, 177.

I

PAYNE, R. W. (1955) L'utilité du test de Rorschach en psychologie clinique, *Rev. Psychol., appl.*, **5**, 255.

PENROSE, L. S. (1944) Mental illness in husband and wife: a contribution to the study of assortative mating in man, *Psychiat. Quart. Suppl.*, **18**, 161.

PETURSSON, E. (1961) A study of parental deprivation and illness in 291 patients, *Int. J. soc. Psychiat.*, **7**, 97.

PIAGET, J. (1929) *The Child's Conception of the World*, London.

—— (1930) *The Child's Conception of Physical Causality*, London.

—— (1932) *The Language and Thought of the Child*, London.

PODOLSKY, E. (1955) The emotional problems of the step-child, *Mental Hygiene* **39**, 49.

POLLAK, O. (1952) *Social Science and Psychotherapy for Children*, New York.

POND, D. A., RYLE, A., and HAMILTON, M. (1963) Marriage and neurosis in a working-class population, *Brit. J. Psychiat.*, **109**, 592.

POST, F. (1962) The social orbit of psychiatric patients, *J. ment. Sci.*, **108**, 759.

POST, F., and WARDLE, J. (1962) Family neurosis and family psychosis, *J. ment. Sci.*, **108**, 147.

PRESTON, G., and ANTIN, R. (1933) A study of the children of psychotic parents, *Amer. J. Orthopsychiat.*, **2**, 231.

PRUGH, D. G., STAUB, E. M., SANDS, H. H., KIRSCHBAUM, R. M., and LENIHAM, E. A. (1953) A study of the emotional reactions of children and families to hospitalization and illness, *Amer. J. Orthopsychiat.*, **23**, 70.

QUERIDO, A. (1959) Forecast and follow-up: an investigation into the clinical, social and mental factors determining the results of hospital treatment, *Brit. J. prev. soc. Med.*, **13**, 33.

RABIN, A. I. (1957) Personal maturity of Kibbutz (Israeli collective settlement) and non-Kibbutz children as reflected in Rorschach findings, *J. project. Techn.*, **21**, 148.

—— (1958) Infants and children under conditions of 'intermittent' mothering in the Kibbutz, *Amer. J. Orthopsychiat.*, **28**, 577.

—— (1959) Attitudes of Kibbutz children to family and parents, *Amer. J. Orthopsychiat.*, **29**, 172.

RADINSKY, E. K. (1961) Children of discharged mental hospital patients, *Children*, **8**, 88.

RAMAGE, M. (1925) Mental health of children of psychotic mothers, Master's Thesis, *Smith Coll. Stud. soc. Work* (cited Preston, G. and Antin, R.).

RANK, B., PUTNAM, M. C., and ROCHLIN, B. (1947) The significance of the 'emotional climate' in the early feeding difficulties, *Psychosom. Med.*, **10**, 279.

REGISTRAR GENERAL (1939-60 incl.) *Statistical Review of England and Wales*, Volumes for 1938 to 1959 inclusive, *Part I*, Tables, Medical, London,

—— (1939-60 incl.) *Statistical Review of England and Wales*, Volumes for 1938 to 1959 inclusive. *Part II*, Tables, Population, London.

—— (1951) *Statistical Review of England and Wales for the Two Years 1946-1947* Text, Vol. 1, Medical, London.

—— (1951) *Decennial Supplement, England and Wales*, Life Tables, London.

—— (1953) *Statistical Review of England and Wales for the Year 1949*, Supplement on General Morbidity, Cancer and Mental Health, London.

—— (1956) *Census 1951, England and Wales, Classification of Occupations*, London.

—— (1958) *Decennial Supplement, England and Wales 1951, Occupational Mortality*, Part II, Vol. 1, Commentary, London.

—— (1960) *Statistical Review of England and Wales for the Three Years 1954-1956: Supplement on Mental Health*, London.

RHEINGOLD, H. L. (1956) The modification of social responsiveness in institutional babies, *Monogr. Soc. Res. child Developm.*, **21**, No. 63.

RICHARDSON, H. B. (1945) *Patients Have Families*, New York.

ROESSLER, R., and GREENFIELD, N. S. (1961) Incidence of somatic disease in psychiatric patients, *Psychosom. Med.*, **23**, 413.

ROLLMAN-BRANCH, H. S. (1960) On the question of primary object need, *J. Amer. psychoanalytic Assoc.*, **8**, 686.

ROSENTHAL, D. (1962) Familial concordance by sex with respect to schizophrenia, *Psychol. Bull.*, **59**, 401.

ROSENZWEIG, S., and BRAY, D. (1943) Sibling deaths in the anamneses of schizophrenic patients, *Arch. Neurol. Psychiat.*, **49**, 71.

ROSENZWEIG, S., and ISHAM, A. C. (1947) Complementary thematic apperception test patterns in close kin, *Amer. J. Orthopsychiat.*, **17**, 129.

ROWNTREE, G. (1955) Early childhood in broken families, *Population studies*, **8**, 247.

RUTTER, M. (1963a) Some current research issues in American child psychiatry, *Milbank Mem. Fund Quart.*, XLI, 339.

—— (1963b) Psychosocial factors in the short-term prognosis of physical disease: I. Peptic Ulcer, *J. psychosom. Res.*, **7**, 45.

—— (1964) Intelligence and childhood psychiatric disorder, *Brit. J. soc. clin. Psychol.*, **3**, 120.

RUTTER, M., KORN, S., and BIRCH, H. G. (1963) Genetic and environmental factors in the development of 'primary reaction patterns', *Brit. J. soc. clin. Psychol.*, **2**, 161.

RUTTER, M., BIRCH, H. G., THOMAS, A., and CHESS, S. (1964) Temperamental characteristics in infancy and the later development of behavioural disorders, *Brit. J. Psychiat.*, **110**, 651.

SAINSBURY, P., and GRAD, J. (1962) An evaluation of treatment and services, *The Burden on the Community. Epidemiology of Mental Illness. A Symposium*, London.

SAMPSON, H., MESSINGER, S. L., TOWNE, R. D., ROSS, D., LIVSON, F., BOWERS, M-D., COHEN, L., and DORST, K. S. (1961) The mental hospital and marital family ties, *Social Problems*, **9**, 141.

SAMPSON, H., MESSINGER, S. L., and TOWNE, R. D. (1962) The mental hospital and family adaptations, *Psychiat. Quart.*, **36**, 704.

SCARPITTI, F. R., LEFTON, M., DINITZ, S., and PASAMANICK, B. (1964) Problems in a home care study for schizophrenics, *Arch. gen. Psychiat.*, **10**, 143.

SCHAFFER, H. R. (1958) Objective observations of personality development in early infancy, *Brit. J. med. Psychol.*, **31**, 174.

SCHAFFER, H. R., and CALLENDER, W. M. (1959) Psychologic effects of hospitalization in infancy, *Paediatrics*, **24**, 528.

SCHNEIRLA, T. C. (1959) Comparative Psychology, *Encyclopaedia Britannica*.

SCHNEIDER, R. A., GRAY, J. S., and CULMER, C. U. (1950) Psychologic evaluation of surgical patients: a correlation between pre-operative psychometric studies and recovery, *Wisconsin med. J.*, **49**, 285.

SEARS, R. R., PINTLER, M. H., and SEARS, P. S. (1946) Effect of father-separation on pre-school children's doll play aggression, *Child Development*, **17**, 219.

SHARMA, N. (1950) *Gratification Habits in Childhood*, M.D. Thesis, Lucknow.

SHEPHERD, M., FISHER, M., STEIN, L., and KESSEL, W. I. N. (1959), Psychiatric morbidity in an urban group practice, *Proc. roy. Soc. Med.*, **52**, 269.

SHIELDS, J. (1954) Personality differences and neurotic traits in normal twin schoolchildren, *Eugen. Rev.*, **45**, 213.

SILVERMAN, B. (1935) The behaviour of children from broken homes, *Amer. J. Orthopsychiat.*, **5**, 11.

SKLAREW, B. H. (1959) The relationship of early separation from parents to differences in adjustment in adolescent boys and girls, *Psychiatry*, **22**, 399.

SLATER, E. (1953) Psychotic and Neurotic Illness in Twins, *M.R.C. Special Report Series No. 238.*

SOBEL, D. E. (1961) Children of schizophrenic patients: Preliminary observations on early development, *Amer. J. Psychiat.*, **118**, 512.

SPIEGEL, J. P., and BELL, N. (1959) The family of the 'psychiatric' patient, *American Handbook of Psychiatry* (Ed. Arieti, S.), New York.

SPIRO, M. E. (1955) Education in a communal village in Israel, *Amer. J. Orthopsychiat.*, **25**, 283.

SPITZ, R. A. (1946) Anaclitic depression: an enquiry into the genesis of psychiatric conditions in early childhood, II, *Psychoanalyt. Study Child*, **2**, 313.

STENGEL, E. (1960) A comparative study of psychiatric classifications, *Proc. roy. Soc. Med.*, **53**, 123.

STERN, E. S. (1948) The Medea complex: the mother's homicidal wishes to her child, *J. ment. Sci.*, **94**, 321.

STOTT, D. H. (1956) The effects of separation from the mother in early life, *Lancet*, **i**, 624.

SUNIER, A., and MEIJERS, N. A. (1951) The influence of a chronical (*sic*) psychosis of one of the parents upon the development of the child, *Folia Psychiat.* (*Amst.*), **54**, 323.

SUSSEX, J. N. (1963) Factors influencing the emotional impact on children of an acutely psychotic mother in the home, *Southern med. J.*, **56**, 1245.

SUSSEX, J. N., CASSMAN, F., and RAFFEL, S. C. (1963) Adjustment of children with psychotic mothers in the home, *Amer. J. Orthopsychiat.*, **33**, 849.

SZASZ, T. S. (1959) The communication of distress between child and parent, *Brit. J. med. Psychol.*, **32**, 161.

THOM, D. A., and WALKER, G. S. (1921) Epilepsy in the offspring of epileptics, *Amer. J. Psychiat.*, **2**, 613.

THOMAS, A., BIRCH, H. G., CHESS, S., and ROBBINS, L. C. (1961) Individuality in responses of children to similar environmental situations, *Amer. J. Psychiat.*, **117**, 798.

THOMAS, A., BIRCH, H. G., CHESS, S., HERTZIG, M. E., and KORN, S. (1963) *Behavioural Individuality in Early Childhood*, New York.

THORPE, W. H. (1961) Comparative psychology, *Ann. Rev. Psychol.*, **12**, 27.

TREUDLEY, M. (1946) Mental illness and family routines, *Mental Hygiene*, **30**, 34.

ULLMAN, C. A. (1952) Identification of maladjusted school children, *Public Health Mon. No. 7.*

VAN KREVELEN, D. A., Ed. (1964) *Child Psychiatry and Prevention*, Berne and Stuttgart.

VOLKART, E. H. (1957) Bereavement and Mental Health: in *Explorations in Social Psychiatry* (Eds. Leighton, A. H., Clausen, J. A., and Wilson, R. N.), London.

WAHL, C. W. (1954) Some antecedent factors in the family histories of 392 schizophrenics, *Amer. J. Psychiat.*, **110**, 668.

—— (1956) Some antecedent factors in the family histories of 568 male schizophrenics in the United States Navy, *Amer. J. Psychiat.* **113**, 201.

WALLER, W. (1951) *The Family: a Dynamic Interpretation* (revised by Hill, R.), New York.

WARDLE, C. J. (1961) Two generations of broken homes in the genesis of conduct and behaviour disorders in childhood, *Brit. med. J.*, **ii**, 349.

WARREN, W. (1960) Some relationships between the psychiatry of children and of adults, *J. ment. Sci.*, **106**, 815.

WEINSTEIN, E. A., and GEISEL, P. N. (1960) An analysis of sex differences in adjustment, *Child Development*, **31**, 721.

WEISS, J. L., GRUNEBAUM, H. U., and SCHELL, R. E. (1964) Psychotic mothers and their children, *Arch. gen. Psychiat.*, **11**, 90.

WING, J. K., MONCK, E., BROWN, G. W. and CARSTAIRS, C. M. (1964) Morbidity in the community of schizophrenic patients discharged from London mental hospitals in 1959, *Brit. J. Psychiat.*, **110**, 10.

WINNICOTT, D. W. (1961) The effect of psychotic parents on the emotional development of the child, *Brit. J. psychiat. soc. Work*, **6**, 13.

WITMER, H. (1933) Parental behaviour as an index to the probable outcome of treatment in a child guidance clinic, *Amer. J. Orthopsychiat.*, **3**, 431.

WOODWARD, J. (1959) Emotional disturbance of burned children, *Brit. med. J.*, **i**, 1009.

WOOTTON, B. (1959) *Social Science and Social Pathology*, London.

YARROW, L. J. (1961) Maternal deprivation: towards an empirical and conceptual re-evaluation, *Psychol. Bull.*, **58**, 459.

YARROW, M R., CLAUSEN, J. A., and ROBBINS, P. R. (1955), Social meaning of mental illness, *J. social Issues*, **11**, 33.

YARROW, M. R., SCHWARTZ, C. G., MURPHY, M. S., and DEASY, L. C. (1955), Psychological meaning of mental illness in the family, *J. social Issues*, **11**, 12.

YUDKIN, S., and HOLME, A. (1963) *Working Mothers and Their Children*, London.

# APPENDIX (i)

# DEFINITION OF TERMS USED

### 1. PARENTAL PSYCHIATRIC ILLNESS
(i) Any illness for which the person had consulted a psychiatrist who diagnosed it as a psychiatric disorder; or

(ii) Any 'successful' suicide; or

(iii) Any suicidal act for which the person had consulted a doctor.

### 2. PARENTAL PHYSICAL ILLNESS
(i) *'Acute' illness:* Any physical illness which had caused total or partial incapacity to work for a single period exceeding four weeks but less than one year, or which had caused chronic or recurring disability involving a similar period of incapacity over the course of one year. In housewives, any illness judged to have caused a similar degree of impairment of capacity was included. Upper respiratory tract infections were excluded.

(ii) *'Recurrent' illness:* Any condition which had lasted intermittently for one year or longer and which otherwise fulfilled the criteria for 'acute' illness.

(iii) *'Chronic' illness:* Any condition which had *substantially* impaired work capacity (as by causing a change to lighter duties) or social activities and which had lasted continuously for one year or longer.

### 3. PARENT
Any person in the role of parent to the child, other than temporarily, whether or not a true parent. Thus, step-parents, adoptive parents, etc. were included (unless specifically stated otherwise in any context).

### 4. STEP-PARENT
In addition to the normal usage, this term included persons acting as parent to the child and who cohabited with the other parent, although there had been no legal marriage.

### 5. SIBS
Sibs included all those acting as sibs (i.e. including adoptive, foster, half or step-sibs), if they had been present in the home for more than six months. For example, married step-sibs who had, throughout, lived away from home were not included, nor were sibs who had died before the birth of the patient or who had not lived for more than six months during his (or her) lifetime.

### 6. POSITION IN SIBSHIP
This was determined using the definition of sib above.

### 7. FIELDS OF DISTURBANCE OF CHILDREN (based on Cameron, 1955)
A. *Primary habit disorder*
    Disorder of micturition
                defaecation
                eating
                sleeping
                speech

B. *Secondary habit disorder*
      Gratification habits
      Tension habits

C. *Motor disorder*
      Hyperactivity
      Tics or habit spasms
      Any other motor disorder

D. *Disturbed relationships*
      Aggressive manifestations
      Disturbed relationships with father, mother, sibs or peers

E. *School or work disorder*

F. *Conduct disorder*
Disorder in which symptoms include socially unacceptable behaviour:
      Lying
      Truanting
      Wandering from home
      Stealing
      Disobedience
      Destructiveness
      Fighting
      Sexual disorder

G. *Psychic disorder*
Disorder with neurotic symptoms:
      Anxiety
      Depression
      Hysterical symptoms
      Obsessional symptoms

H. *Functional somatic disorder*
Somatic symptoms where no organic pathology thought to be present:
      Abdominal symptoms
      Headache
      Fainting attacks
      Hypochondriasis

I. *Allergic diathesis*
      Hay fever and allergic rhinitis
      Asthma
      Eczema
      Urticaria

8. SYMPTOMS OF THE CHILDREN

Behaviour normal at one age may be abnormal at another, but symptoms were not defined in such terms. Symptoms were defined in their scope, and the opinion of the psychiatrist treating the child was always taken on whether the symptom was abnormal in its context at that age. Symptoms were recorded only if they had been regarded as abnormal.

(i) *Micturition:* Any disturbance of urinary elimination (in practically all cases the complaint was of enuresis).

(ii) *Defaecation:* Any disturbance of alimentary elimination including constipation, diarrhoea or encopresis (in nearly all cases the complaint was of encopresis).

(iii) *Eating:* Any disorder of eating: refusal of food, morbid faddiness, etc.

(iv) *Sleeping:* Any disorder of sleeping; insomnia, nightmares, night terrors, somnambulism, etc.

(v) *Speech:* Any disorder of speech; stammering, stuttering, baby talk, etc.

(vi) *Gratification habits:* Thumb sucking, tongue sucking, rocking, or masturbation.

(vii) *Tension habits:* Nail biting, picking, scratching, or head banging.

(viii) *Hyperactivity:* Abnormal motor hyperactivity or restlessness.

(ix) *Tics:* Tics or habit spasms.

(x) *Other motor symptoms:* Hypoactivity or other motor disorder (excluding 'organic' symptoms such as paresis).

(xi) *Aggressive manifestations:* Screaming, breath-holding, temper tantrums or aggressiveness.

(xii) *Disturbed relationship with father:* Any manifest disturbance in relationship with father or father substitute.

(xiii) *Disturbed relationship with mother:* Any manifest disturbance in relationship with mother or mother substitute.

(xiv) *Disturbed relationship with sibs:* Any manifest disturbance in relationship with sibs.

(xv) *Disturbed relationship with peers:* Any manifest disturbance in relationship with peers.

(xvi) *School or work record:* Any manifest disturbance in relation to school or work (excluding truanting).

(xvii) *Lying:* Deceit or telling falsehoods to a morbid extent.

(xviii) *Truanting:* Absence from school without leave and without the knowledge of parents (thus excluding 'school phobia').

(xix) *Wandering from home:* Running away or wandering from home, or staying out at night.

(xx) *Stealing:* Any form of theft.

(xxi) *Disobedience:* Refusal to obey parental instructions—to an extent regarded as morbid.

(xxii) *Destructiveness:* Destructive behaviour, including fire-setting.

(xxiii) *Fighting:* Including bullying and attacking adults or other children.

(xxiv) *Sexual Disorders:* Any morbid deviant sexual activity: including homosexual behaviour, heterosexual assault, fetishism, transvestism, etc.

(xxv) *Anxiety:* See under parental symptoms.

(xxvi) *Depression:* See under parental symptoms.

(xxvii) *Hysterical symptoms:* See under parental symptoms.

(xxviii) *Obsessional symptoms:* See under parental symptoms.

(xxix) *Abdominal symptoms:* Abdominal pain, nausea, vomiting, etc.

(xxx) *Headache:* Headache of 'functional' origin.

(xxxi) *Fainting attacks:* Any fainting attacks.

(xxxii) *Hypochondriasis:* Including other somatic symptoms of 'functional' origin.

(xxxiii) *Allergic diathesis:* Hay fever, allergic rhinitis, asthma, eczema, or urticaria.

9. DIAGNOSIS OF CHILD

*Neurotic illness:* Any illness diagnosed as neurotic under I.C.D. headings 310 to 314.

*Neurotic behaviour disorder:* Any disorder in which 'neurotic' symptoms were predominant.' 'Neurotic' symptoms for this purpose included symptoms i–x and xxv–xxxiii, as listed.

*Conduct behaviour disorder:* Any disorder in which 'antisocial' symptoms were predominant. 'Antisocial' symptoms, for this purpose, included symptoms xi and xvii–xxiv, as listed. Symptoms xii–xvi might be classed as either neurotic or antisocial, according to their setting and accompanying symptoms.

*Mixed behaviour disorder:* Any disorder in which there was such an admixture of neurotic and antisocial symptoms that neither could be said to predominate. In many cases, there was some admixture of symptoms but only the few cases in which neither group was predominant were included in this category.

### 10. DIAGNOSIS OF THE PARENT

*Schizophrenia:* I.C.D. codings 300 and 303.

*Depression:* I.C.D. codings 301.1, 301.2, 303, and 314.

*Personality disorder:* I.C.D. codings 320, 321, 326.4 and 083.1 (the last used in one case only).

*Neurosis:* I.C.D. codings 310–313, and 315–318.

*Other:* Any other coding.

*Suicidal act:* Any effort to injure the self in such a way that the subject might have expected to die and for which he received medical attention.

### 11. SYMPTOMS OF PARENT

(a) *Anxiety:* A subjective state of expectation, but not certainty, that something unpleasant will happen—including morbid fears, tension and agitation.

(b) *Depression:* Morbid depression of mood.

(c) *Delusions:* Morbid beliefs not justified by the facts and not shakeable by reason (but excluding hypochondriasis).

(d) *Hallucinations:* False perceptions related to auditory, tactile, olfactory or visual senses.

(e) *Obsessional symptoms:* Compulsive actions or thoughts recognized by the patient as unreasonable and resisted.

(f) *Hysterical symptoms:* Somatic symptoms (excluding those pertaining to the autonomic nervous system) for which no organic basis was found and which were thought to be psychogenic in origin.

(g) *Somatic symptoms:* Hypochondriasis—physically unjustified or exaggerated bodily complaints—and functional somatic symptoms pertaining to the autonomic nervous system (faints, functional dyspepsia, anorexia, etc.)

(h) *Suicidal act or gesture:* Any self-destructive act (whether or not completed).

(i) *Other symptoms:* Any other symptoms.

(j) *Symptoms involving children:* Any symptoms which directly involved the child in some way. Excluded were disordered relationships with children which were not part of the psychiatric illness.

(k) *Symptoms involving spouse:* Any symptoms which directly involved the spouse in some way. Excluded were disordered relationships with spouse which were not part of the psychiatric illness.

(l) *Symptoms involving others:* Any symptoms which directly involved others in some way. Excluded were disordered relationships with others which were not part of the psychiatric illness.

### 12. DURATION OF DISORDER

The period between the time of onset of the first overt symptom of the present psychiatric illness and the time of first attending The Maudsley Hospital.

Coded as: (*a*)  Less than 6 months

(*b*)  6 months or more but less than 3 years

(*c*)  3 years or more

13. DURATION OF TREATMENT

The period from first attendance at The Maudsley Hospital until last attendance (not including attendances for follow-up).

Coded as: (a) Less than 4 months
(b) 4 months or more but less than 1 year
(c) 1 year or more

14. NUMBER OF ATTENDANCES

Number of occasions when the child was seen by the psychiatrist (meetings between parents and psychiatric social workers not included).

Coded as: (a) 1–6 interviews
(b) 7–20 interviews
(c) 21 or more interviews

# METHOD OF CALCULATING THE EXPECTED BEREAVEMENT RATE AMONG PARENTS OF CHILDREN ATTENDING THE MAUDSLEY HOSPITAL

THE REGISTRAR GENERAL publishes annually, in the *Statistical Review for England and Wales*, (a) the estimated mid-year population (Part II, Tables, Population), and (b) the number of deaths (Part I, Tables, Medical), in each case according to age, sex and marital status. From these data a table of *specific mortality ratios* was compiled for the general population, by age, sex and marital status, for each of the years 1938–59 inclusive, which cover the lifetime of the children in the sample in the present survey.[1]

The data obtained in the sample included, for each child, (a) the year of first attendance, (b) the age at that time, (c) the age of parents at that time, and (d) the age at death of deceased parents, and the year in which they died. Tables were compiled for each year from 1938 to 1959, showing the number of parents alive on 1 January, according to age, sex and marital status.

The expected number of deaths in each year in the population of parents was calculated by applying the specific mortality ratios to the data in these tables. By summing these numbers the expected total number of parental deaths in the lifetime of the children in the sample up to the time of first referral could be estimated.[2]

These estimations may be expressed algebraically, as follows:

In the general population, for married males aged $a$ in year $r$, the specific mortality ratio:

$$Sa.r = \frac{Ma.r}{Pa.r}$$

where Ma.r = number of deaths during year $r$ of married males aged $a$

Pa.r = mid-year population of married males aged $a$.

If $x_{a.r}$ is the number of married males who were parents of children in the sample and aged $a$ on 1 January of year $r$ (the children having been born on or before 30 June of that year), the expected number of deaths among these fathers during year $r$ will be:

$$x_{a.r}.S_{a.r}.$$

---

[1] For the war years, data referring to non-civilian deaths were not analysed according to marital status, instead, specific mortality ratios were computed, according to age and sex.

[2] In these calculations, the two fathers who had died before the birth of the patient were not included. In the 47 cases where the age of one parent was not known, it was assumed that the father was 3 years older than the mother (this being the difference between the mean ages of fathers and mothers). In the 26 cases where the age of neither parent was known, the ages were assumed to be those of the mean ages of fathers and mothers of children of the same age as that patient (the mean ages being those for the whole group of Maudsley 'disturbed' children).

So the total number of expected deaths among all married fathers of children in the sample will be:

$$D_{E.M.} = \sum_{a=17}^{a=74} \sum_{r=1938}^{r=1959} x_{a.r.} S_{a.r.}$$

Similarly was estimated the total number of expected deaths among the fathers who were divorced ($D_{E.D.}$) and those who were widowed ($D_{E.W.}$)

The total number of expected deaths among all fathers of children in the sample is:

$$D_E = D_{E.M.} + D_{E.D.} + D_{E.W.}$$

The total number of expected deaths among fathers was then compared with the total number of observed deaths among fathers. The significance of the difference was estimated by chi-square.

Identical methods were used to compare observed and expected numbers of deaths among mothers of children in the sample.

# APPENDIX (iii)

# ADDITIONAL TABLES

### TABLE 2.1
### MATCHING FOR AGE IN THE MAUDSLEY AND DENTAL GROUPS

| Age (years) | Groups | | | |
| --- | --- | --- | --- | --- |
| | Maudsley children | | Dental children | |
| | No. | % | No. | % |
| 5 or less | 15 | (5·8) | 8 | (5·5) |
| 6–7 | 35 | (13·5) | 20 | (13·8) |
| 8–9 | 39 | (15·1) | 20 | (13·8) |
| 10–11 | 70 | (27·0) | 39 | (26·9) |
| 12–13 | 100 | (38·6) | 58 | (40·0) |
| Total | 259 | | 145 | |

### TABLE 2.2
### MATCHING FOR SOCIAL CLASS IN THE MAUDSLEY AND DENTAL GROUPS

| Social class | Groups | | | |
| --- | --- | --- | --- | --- |
| | Maudsley children | | Dental children | |
| | No. | % | No. | % |
| I and II | 50 | (19·3) | 29 | (20·0) |
| III | 135 | (52·1) | 77 | (53·1) |
| IV | 28 | (10·8) | 19 | (13·1) |
| V | 35 | (13·5) | 20 | (13·8) |
| Not known | 11 | (4·3) | — | — |
| Total | 259 | | 145 | |

### TABLE 2.3
### MATCHING FOR AGE IN THE MAUDSLEY AND PAEDIATRIC GROUPS

| Age (years) | Groups | | | |
| --- | --- | --- | --- | --- |
| | Maudsley children | | Paediatric children | |
| | No. | % | No. | % |
| 5 or less | 15 | (9·5) | 7 | (8·7) |
| 6–7 | 35 | (22·0) | 18 | (22·5) |
| 8–9 | 39 | (24·5) | 20 | (25·0) |
| 10–11 | 70 | (44·0) | 35 | (43·8) |
| Total | 159 | | 80 | |

TABLE 2.4

MATCHING FOR SOCIAL CLASS IN THE MAUDSLEY AND PAEDIATRIC GROUPS

| Social class | Groups Maudsley children No. % | Paediatric children No. % |
|---|---|---|
| I and II | 29 (18·2) | 16 (20·0) |
| III | 88 (55·4) | 44 (55·0) |
| IV | 17 (10·7) | 10 (12·5) |
| V | 18 (11·3) | 10 (12·5) |
| Not known | 7 (4·4) | — — |
| Total | 159 | 80 |

TABLE 3.3

MATCHING FOR AGE IN DISTURBED AND NON-DISTURBED GROUPS

| Age (years) | Groups Disturbed No. % | Non-disturbed No. % |
|---|---|---|
| 5 or less | 38 (7·1) | 7 (7·0) |
| 6–7 | 70 (13·2) | 14 (14·0) |
| 8–9 | 95 (17·9) | 18 (18·0) |
| 10–11 | 135 (25·4) | 25 (25·0) |
| 12–13 | 194 } (36·5) | 24 } (36·0) |
| 14 | — } | 12 } |
| Total | 532 | 100 |

TABLE 6.1
AGES OF CHILDREN

| Groups | Age (in years) | | | | | | | Totals |
|---|---|---|---|---|---|---|---|---|
| | 5 or less No. % | 6–7 No. % | 8–9 No. % | 10–11 No. % | 12–13 No. % | 14–15 No. % | 16–17 No. % | |
| Psychiatric | 14 (10·2) | 15 (10·9) | 22 (16·1) | 26 (19·0) | 33 (24·1) | 24 (17·5) | 3 (2·2) | 137 |
| Other | 23 (3·9) | 52 (8·8) | 73 (12·3) | 105 (17·7) | 160 (27·0) | 124 (21·0) | 55 (9·3) | 592 |

Chi-square=18·49  6 d.f.  p<0·01

TABLE 6.6
INTELLIGENCE QUOTIENTS OF CHILDREN

| Scores | Groups Psychiatric No. % | Other No. % | Significance |
|---|---|---|---|
| 79 or less | 10 (8·8) | 55 (11·0) | N.S. |
| 80–89 | 19 (16·7) | 104 (20·9) | N.S. |
| 90–99 | 27 (23·7) | 105 (21·1) | N.S. |
| 100–109 | 28 (24·5) | 101 (20·2) | N.S. |
| 110–119 | 16 (14·0) | 77 (15·4) | N.S. |
| 120 or more | 14 (12·3) | 57 (11·4) | N.S. |
| Total | 114 | 499 | |
| Not known | 23 (16·8) | 93 (15·7) | |
| Total | 137 | 592 | |

### TABLE 6.8
### PRIMARY HABIT DISORDER

| Symptoms | Groups | | | | Significance | |
|---|---|---|---|---|---|---|
| | Psychiatric | | Other | | Critical ratio | p |
| | No. | % | No. | % | | |
| Total with primary habit disorder | 93 | (67·9) | 330 | (55·7) | 2·596 | <0·01 |
| *Disorder of* | | | | | | |
| micturition | 31 | (22·6) | 111 | (18·7) | N.S. | |
| defaecation | 14 | (10·2) | 43 | (7·3) | N.S. | |
| eating | 23 | (16·8) | 83 | (14·0) | N.S. | |
| sleeping | 60 | (43·8) | 182 | (30·7) | 2·977 | <0·01 |
| speech | 11 | (8·0) | 41 | (6·9) | N.S. | |
| Total children | 137 | | 592 | | | |

### TABLE 6.9
### SECONDARY HABIT DISORDER

| Symptoms | Groups | | | | Significance | |
|---|---|---|---|---|---|---|
| | Psychiatric | | Other | | Critical ratio | p |
| | No. | % | No. | % | | |
| Total with secondary habit disorder | 88 | (64·2) | 274 | (46·3) | 3·729 | <0·001 |
| gratification habits | 28 | (19·7) | 63 | (10·6) | 2·935 | <0·01 |
| tension habits | 77 | (56·2) | 249 | (42·1) | 3·00 | <0·01 |
| Total children | 137 | | 592 | | | |

### TABLE 6.10
### MOTOR SYMPTOMS

| Symptoms | Groups | | | | Significance | |
|---|---|---|---|---|---|---|
| | Psychiatric | | Other | | Critical ratio | p |
| | No. | % | No. | % | | |
| Total with motor symptoms | 55 | (40·2) | 185 | (31·2) | 2·00 | <0·05 |
| hyperactivity | 49 | (35·8) | 155 | (26·2) | 2·286 | <0·03 |
| tics | 10 | (7·3) | 45 | (7·6) | N.S. | |
| other motor symptoms | — | — | 2 | (0·3) | — | |
| Total children | 137 | | 592 | | | |

TABLE 6.11
DISTURBED RELATIONSHIPS

| Symptoms | Groups | | Significance | |
| | Psychiatric No. % | Other No. % | Critical ratio | p |
| --- | --- | --- | --- | --- |
| Total with disturbed relationships | 123 (*89·8*) | 472 (*79·7*) | 2·73 | <0·01 |
| temper tantrums/ aggression | 81 (*59·1*) | 261 (*44·1*) | 3·192 | <0·01 |
| disturbed relationship | | | | |
| father | 45 (*31·9*) | 213 (*36·0*) | N.S. | |
| mother | 84 (*61·3*) | 306 (*51·7*) | 2·043 | <0·05 |
| sibs | 54 (*39·3*) | 149 (*25·2*) | 3·357 | <0·001 |
| peers | 42 (*30·7*) | 190 (*32·1*) | N.S. | |
| Total children | 137 | 592 | | |

TABLE 6.12
PSYCHIC SYMPTOMS

| Symptoms | Groups | | Significance | |
| | Psychiatric No. % | Other No. % | Critical ratio | p |
| --- | --- | --- | --- | --- |
| Total with psychic symptoms | 89 (*65·0*) | 295 (*49·8*) | 3·234 | <0·01 |
| anxiety | 65 (*47·5*) | 194 (*32·8*) | 3·1961 | <0·01 |
| hysterical symptoms | 5 (*3·7*) | 22 (*3·7*) | N.S. | |
| obsessional symptoms | 11 (*8·0*) | 41 (*6·9*) | N.S. | |
| depression | 36 (*26·3*) | 153 (*25·8*) | N.S. | |
| Total children | 137 | 592 | | |

TABLE 6.13
CONDUCT DISORDER

| Symptoms | Groups | | Significance | |
| | Psychiatric No. % | Other No. % | Critical ratio | p |
| --- | --- | --- | --- | --- |
| Total with conduct disorder | 92 (*67·2*) | 367 (*62·0*) | N.S. | |
| lying | 39 (*28·5*) | 150 (*25·3*) | N.S. | |
| truanting | 22 (*16·1*) | 107 (*18·0*) | N.S. | |
| wandering from home | 16 (*11·7*) | 65 (*11·0*) | N.S. | |
| stealing | 43 (*31·4*) | 184 (*31·1*) | N.S. | |
| disobedience | 59 (*43·1*) | 181 (*30·6*) | 2·841 | <0·01 |
| destructiveness | 25 (*18·2*) | 90 (*15·2*) | N.S. | |
| fighting | 18 (*13·1*) | 62 (*10·5*) | N.S. | |
| sexual disorder | 6 (*4·4*) | 48 (*8·1*) | N.S. | |
| Total children | 137 | 592 | | |

### TABLE 6.14
### SCHOOL OR WORK DISORDER

| Symptoms | Groups | | Significance |
| --- | --- | --- | --- |
| | Psychiatric | Other | Critical ratio  p |
| | No.  % | No.  % | |
| School or work disorder | 54 (*39·4*) | 246 (*41·5*) | N.S. |
| Total children | 137 | 592 | |

### TABLE 6.15
### FUNCTIONAL SOMATIC SYMPTOMS

| Symptoms | Groups | | Significance |
| --- | --- | --- | --- |
| | Psychiatric | Other | Critical ratio  p |
| | No.  % | No.  % | |
| Total with functional symptoms | 25 (*18·3*) | 108 (*18·2*) | N.S. |
| abdominal pain, etc. | 20 (*14·6*) | 88 (*14·9*) | N.S. |
| headache | 5 (*3·7*) | 21 (*3·5*) | N.S. |
| fainting | 4 (*2·9*) | 11 (*1·9*) | N.S. |
| hypochondriasis | 2 (*1·5*) | 2 (*0·3*) | N.S. |
| Total children | 137 | 592 | |

### TABLE 6.16
### ALLERGIC DIATHESIS

| Symptoms | Groups | | Significance |
| --- | --- | --- | --- |
| | Psychiatric | Other | Critical ratio  p |
| | No.  % | No.  % | |
| Allergic diathesis | 8 (*5·8*) | 21 (*3·5*) | N.S. |
| Total children | 137 | 592 | |

### TABLE 6.19
### AGE OF CHILDREN

| Age | Groups | | |
| --- | --- | --- | --- |
| | Recurrent | Chronic | Other |
| | No.  % | No.  % | No.  % |
| 5 or less | 1 (*1·1*) | 3 (*3·2*) | 34 (*6·2*) |
| 6–7 | 10 (*10·5*) | 7 (*7·4*) | 53 (*9·7*) |
| 8–9 | 12 (*12·6*) | 10 (*10·5*) | 73 (*13·3*) |
| 10–11 | 19 (*20·0*) | 16 (*16·8*) | 100 (*18·2*) |
| 12–13 | 25 (*26·3*) | 31 (*32·6*) | 138 (*25·1*) |
| 14–15 | 23 (*24·2*) | 19 (*20·0*) | 107 (*19·5*) |
| 16–17 | 5 (*5·3*) | 9 (*9·5*) | 44 (*8·0*) |
| Total | 95 | 95 | 549 |

Chi-square not significant

K

TABLE 6.20
SOCIAL CLASS

| Social Class | Recurrent No. % | Groups Chronic No. % | Other No. % |
|---|---|---|---|
| I and II | 14 (15·7) | 19 (20·9) | 116 (22·6) |
| III | 43 (48·4) | 42 (46·2) | 265 (51·7) |
| IV | 14 (15·7) | 17 (18·7) | 68 (13·3) |
| V | 18 (20·2) | 13 (14·3) | 64 (12·5) |
| Total | 89 | 91 | 513 |
| Not known | 6 | 4 | 36 |

Chi-square = 7·817   6 d.f.   p<0·3

TABLE 8.5
AGE OF THE AFFECTED PARENT AND DISORDER IN THE CHILD

| Age (years) | Groups (key below) 1 No. % | 2 No. % | 3 No. % | Significance Critical ratio  p |
|---|---|---|---|---|
| 24 or less | 1 (2·1) | 10 (5·9) | 3 (9·7) | N.S. |
| 25–29 | 7 (14·6) | 29 (17·2) | 2 (6·5) | N.S. |
| 30–34 | 12 (25·0) | 59 (34·9) | 10 (32·2) | N.S. |
| 35–39 | 16 (33·3) | 24 (14·2) | 9 (29·0) | 2·06   <0·04 |
| 40–44 | 4 (8·3) | 29 (17·2) | 2 (6·5) | N.S. |
| 45–49 | 6 (12·5) | 12 (7·1) | 4 (12·9) | N.S. |
| 50 or over | 2 (4·2) | 6 (3·5) | 1 (3·2) | N.S. |
| Total | 48 | 169 | 31 | |

KEY:  1—Parents of the children attending The Maudsley Hospital
(study group)
2—Control group—parents with 'normal' children
3—Control group—parents with psychiatrically ill children

TABLE 8.6
SOCIAL CLASS OF THE AFFECTED PARENT AND DISORDER IN THE
CHILD

| Social class | Groups (key above) 1 No. % | 2 No. % | 3 No. % | Significance Critical ratio  p |
|---|---|---|---|---|
| I and II | 10 (23·3) | 28 (19·0) | 4 (12·9) | N.S. |
| III | 19 (44·2) | 91 (61·9) | 17 (54·9) | 2·913   <0·04 |
| IV | 8 (18·6) | 16 (10·9) | 6 (19·4) | N.S. |
| V | 6 (13·9) | 12 (8·2) | 3 (9·7) | N.S. |
| Total | 43 | 147 | 30 | |
| Not known | 5 | 22 | 1 | |

### TABLE 8.7
#### IN- AND OUT-PATIENT CARE IN THE STUDY AND CONTROL GROUPS

| Care | Groups (key above) | | | | | Significance |
|---|---|---|---|---|---|---|
| | *I* | | *2* | | *3* | Critical ratio   p |
| | No. % | | No. % | | No. % | |
| In-patient | 17 (35·4) | | 58 (34·3) | | 13 (41·9) | N.S. |
| Out-patient only | 31 (64·6) | | 111 (65·7) | | 18 (58·1) | N.S. |
| Total | 48 | | 169 | | 31 | |

(For the purpose of this study, the few patients treated in the day hospital were included as out-patients)

### TABLE 9.5
#### DIAGNOSIS OF PARENT AND FIELD OF DISORDER IN THE CHILD

| Field of Disorder (in the child) | Diagnosis of Parent (key below) | | | | | |
|---|---|---|---|---|---|---|
| | Sch. | D. | N. | P.D. | S.A. | O or N.K. |
| | No. % | No. % | No. % | No. % | No. % | No. % |
| Primary habits | 6 (54·5) | 36 (83·7) | 32 (76·2) | 30 (76·9) | 8 (66·7) | 15 (62·5) |
| Secondary habits | 3 (27·3) | 30 (69·7) | 28 (66·7) | 31 (79·5) | 9 (75·0) | 12 (50·0) |
| Motor | 2 (18·2) | 17 (39·5) | 20 (47·6) | 17 (43·6) | 4 (33·3) | 12 (50·0) |
| Personal relationships | 9 (81·8) | 38 (88·4) | 40 (95·2) | 37 (94·9) | 10 (83·3) | 22 (91·7) |
| School/Work | 3 (27·3) | 17 (39·5) | 25 (59·5) | 14 (35·9) | 4 (33·3) | 6 (25·0) |
| Conduct | 6 (54·5) | 27 (62·8) | 28 (66·7) | 30 (76·9) | 8 (66·7) | 15 (62·5) |
| Psychic | 8 (72·7) | 22 (51·2) | 29 (69·0) | 23 (59·0) | 9 (75·0) | 16 (66·7) |
| Somatic | 2 (18·2) | 7 (16·3) | 8 (19·0) | 8 (20·5) | 3 (25·0) | 6 (25·0) |
| Allergic | — (—) | 2 (4·7) | 5 (11·9) | 2 (5·1) | — (—) | 1 (4·2) |
| Total | 11 | 43 | 42 | 39 | 12 | 24 |

No significant differences

KEY:   Sch.   Schizophrenia     D.     Depression
       N.   Neurosis           P.D.   Personality disorder
       S.A.   Suicidal act       O. or N.K.   Other or not known

### TABLE 9.6
#### DIAGNOSIS OF PARENT AND SYMPTOMS OF THE CHILD

| Symptoms of Child | Diagnosis of Parent (key above) | | | | | |
|---|---|---|---|---|---|---|
| | Sch. | D. | N. | P.D. | S.A. | O. or N.K. |
| | No. % | No. % | No. % | No. % | No. % | No. % |
| Eating | 1 (9·1) | 8 (18·6) | 9 (21·4) | 7 (17·9) | 4 (33·3) | 4 (16·7) |
| Sleeping | 3 (27·3) | 24 (55·8) | 24 (57·1) | 16 (41·0) | 7 (58·3) | 7 (29·2) |
| Speech | 1 (9·1) | 7 (16·3) | 5 (11·9) | 4 (10·3) | 2 (16·7) | 2 (8·3) |
| Micturition | 1 (9·1) | 8 (18·6) | 12 (28·6) | 15 (38·5) | 1 (8·3) | 7 (29·2) |
| Defaecation | — ( ) | 4 (9·3) | 4 (9·5) | 9 (23·1) | — ( ) | 4 (16·7) |
| Gratification habits | 2 (18·2) | 9 (20·9) | 10 (23·8) | 11 (28·2) | 1 (8·3) | 4 (16·7) |
| Tension habits | 2 (18·2) | 27 (62·8) | 25 (59·5) | 26 (66·7) | 9 (75·0) | 9 (37·5) |
| Hyperactivity | 2 (18·2) | 16 (37·2) | 16 (38·1) | 13 (33·3) | 3 (25·0) | 11 (45·8) |
| Tics | 1 (9·1) | 5 (11·6) | 5 (11·9) | 5 (12·8) | 1 (8·3) | 2 (8·3) |
| Aggression | 6 (54·5) | 25 (58·1) | 26 (61·9) | 23 (59·0) | 4 (33·3) | 11 (45·8) |
| Disturbed relationship | | | | | | |
| mother | 4 (36·4) | 25 (58·1) | 32 (76·2) | 25 (64·1) | 6 (50·0) | 14 (58·3) |
| father | 4 (36·4) | 17 (39·5) | 19 (45·2) | 20 (51·3) | 4 (33·3) | 12 (50·0) |
| sibs | 3 (27·3) | 14 (32·6) | 22 (52·4) | 17 (43·6) | 1 (8·3) | 9 (37·5) |
| peers | 3 (27·3) | 12 (27·9) | 14 (33·3) | 10 (25·6) | 5 (41·7) | 7 (29·2) |
| School | 3 (27·3) | 17 (39·5) | 25 (59·5) | 14 (35·9) | 4 (33·3) | 6 (25·0) |
| Lying | 1 (9·1) | 15 (34·9) | 13 (31·0) | 13 (33·3) | 3 (25·0) | 4 (16·7) |
| Truanting | 1 (9·1) | 6 (14·0) | 9 (21·4) | 5 (12·8) | 2 (16·7) | 1 (4·2) |
| Runaway | — ( ) | 2 (4·7) | 5 (11·9) | 6 (15·4) | 2 (16·7) | 4 (16·7) |
| Theft | 2 (18·2) | 17 (39·5) | 10 (23·8) | 18 (46·2) | 5 (41·7) | 7 (29·2) |
| Disobedience | 3 (27·3) | 14 (32·6) | 21 (50·0) | 17 (43·6) | 4 (33·3) | 13 (54·2) |
| Destructiveness | 4 (36·4) | 6 (14·0) | 8 (19·0) | 8 (20·5) | 2 (16·7) | 4 (16·7) |
| Fighting | 3 (27·3) | 6 (14·0) | 10 (23·8) | 5 (12·8) | 3 (25·0) | 3 (12·5) |
| Sexual | — ( ) | 3 (7·0) | 6 (14·3) | 2 (5·1) | — ( ) | — ( ) |
| Anxiety | 7 (63·6) | 17 (39·5) | 24 (57·1) | 17 (43·6) | 8 (66·7) | 10 (41·7) |
| Depression | 4 (36·4) | 7 (16·3) | 12 (28·6) | 11 (28·2) | 3 (25·0) | 8 (33·3) |
| Hysterical symptoms | — ( ) | 1 (2·3) | 2 (4·8) | 1 (2·6) | — ( ) | 2 (8·3) |
| Obsessional symptoms | 1 (9·1) | 3 (7·0) | 4 (9·5) | — ( ) | 1 (8·3) | 4 (16·7) |
| Headache | 1 (9·1) | 1 (2·3) | 3 (7·1) | 3 (7·7) | — ( ) | 2 (8·3) |
| Abdominal pain, etc. | 2 (18·2) | 5 (11·6) | 5 (11·9) | 5 (12·8) | 3 (25·0) | 4 (16·7) |
| Fainting | — ( ) | 1 (2·3) | 3 (7·1) | 2 (5·1) | — ( ) | 1 (4·2) |
| Hypochondriasis | — ( ) | 1 (2·3) | — ( ) | 1 (2·6) | — ( ) | 1 (4·2) |
| Allergic | — ( ) | 2 (4·7) | 5 (11·9) | 2 (5·1) | 2 (16·7) | 1 (4·2) |
| Total | 11 | 43 | 42 | 39 | 12 | 24 |

No significant differences

For TABLE 9.7 see p. 140.

| Symptoms of Child | I | | II | | III | | IV | | V | |
|---|---|---|---|---|---|---|---|---|---|---|
| | No. | % | No. | % | No. | % | No. | % | No. | % |
| Eating | 13 | (20·3) | 12 | (16·2) | 7 | (20·0) | 6 | (14·3) | 2 | (15·4) |
| Sleeping | 34 | (53·1) | 36 | (48·6) | 15 | (42·9) | 19 | (45·2) | 3 | (23·1) |
| Speech | 7 | (10·9) | 9 | (12·2) | 4 | (11·4) | 7 | (16·7) | 1 | (7·7) |
| Micturition | 19 | (29·7) | 18 | (24·3) | 11 | (31·4) | 11 | (26·2) | 5 | (38·5) |
| Defaecation | 9 | (14·1) | 9 | (12·2) | 7 | (20·0) | 9 | (21·4) | 3 | (23·1) |
| Gratification habits | 13 | (20·3) | 17 | (23·0) | 5 | (14·3) | 9 | (21·4) | 5 | (38·5) |
| Tension habits | 40 | (62·5) | 46 | (62·2) | 25 | (71·4) | 24 | (57·1) | 6 | (46·2) |
| Hyperactivity | 22 | (34·4) | 26 | (35·1) | 16 | (45·7) | 14 | (33·3) | 6 | (46·2) |
| Tics | 8 | (12·5) | 5 | (6·8) | 4 | (11·4) | 5 | (11·9) | — | (—) |
| Aggression | 39 | (60·9) | 42 | (56·8) | 21 | (60·0) | 27 | (64·3) | 8 | (61·5) |
| Disturbed relationship | | | | | | | | | | |
| mother | 48 | (75·0) | 47 | (63·5) | 25 | (71·4) | 29 | (69·0) | 5 | (38·5) |
| father | 23 | (35·9) | 30 | (40·5) | 19 | (54·3) | 20 | (47·6) | 5 | (38·5) |
| sibs | 29 | (45·3) | 30 | (40·5) | 17 | (48·6) | 14 | (33·3) | 3 | (23·1) |
| peers | 15 | (23·4) | 20 | (27·0) | 11 | (31·4) | 12 | (28·6) | 7 | (53·8) |
| School | 31 | (48·4) | 34 | (45·9) | 14 | (40·0) | 20 | (47·6) | 3 | (23·1) |
| Lying | 19 | (29·7) | 22 | (29·7) | 9 | (25·7) | 12 | (28·6) | 5 | (38·5) |
| Truanting | 11 | (17·2) | 13 | (17·6) | 7 | (20·0) | 6 | (14·3) | 3 | (23·1) |
| Runaway | 9 | (14·1) | 10 | (13·5) | 4 | (11·4) | 4 | (9·5) | 3 | (23·1) |
| Theft | 17 | (26·6) | 26 | (35·1) | 14 | (40·0) | 13 | (31·0) | 8 | (61·5) |
| Disobedience | 33 | (51·6) | 29 | (39·2) | 18 | (51·4) | 25 | (59·5) | 6 | (46·2) |
| Destructiveness | 13 | (20·3) | 16 | (21·6) | 8 | (22·9) | 12 | (28·6) | 4 | (30·8) |
| Fighting | 13 | (20·3) | 13 | (17·6) | 6 | (17·1) | 7 | (16·7) | 3 | (23·1) |
| Sexual | 4 | (6·3) | 7 | (9·5) | 3 | (8·6) | 3 | (7·1) | 1 | (7·7) |
| Anxiety | 31 | (48·4) | 33 | (44·6) | 19 | (54·3) | 22 | (52·4) | 6 | (46·2) |
| Depression | 17 | (26·6) | 15 | (20·3) | 12 | (34·3) | 12 | (28·6) | 2 | (15·4) |
| Hysterical symptoms | 1 | (1·6) | 1 | (1·4) | — | ( ) | — | ( ) | 1 | (7·7) |
| Obsessional symptoms | 6 | (9·4) | 5 | (6·8) | 3 | (8·6) | 2 | (4·8) | — | ( ) |
| Headache | 3 | (4·7) | 4 | (5·4) | 3 | (8·6) | 2 | (4·8) | — | ( ) |
| Abdominal pain, etc. | 10 | (15·6) | 11 | (14·9) | 6 | (17·1) | 5 | (11·9) | — | ( ) |
| Fainting | 2 | (3·1) | 2 | (2·7) | — | ( ) | 2 | (4·8) | — | ( ) |
| Hypochondriasis | — | ( ) | 1 | (1·4) | — | ( ) | — | ( ) | — | ( ) |
| Allergic | 6 | (9·4) | 6 | (8·1) | 1 | (2·9) | 4 | (9·5) | — | ( ) |
| Total | 64 | | 74 | | 35 | | 42 | | 13 | |

No significant

KEY:
| | | | |
|---|---|---|---|
| I | Anxiety | VII | Hallucinations |
| II | Depression | VIII | Obsessional symptoms |
| III | Disturbed relationship Spouse | IX | Hysterical symptoms |
| IV | Disturbed relationship Child | X | Somatic symptoms |
| V | Disturbed relationship Others | XI | Suicidal acts or gestures |
| VI | Delusions | XII | Other symptoms |

9.8
## SYMPTOMS OF THE CHILD

(key below)

| VI | | VII | | VIII | | IX | | X | | XI | | XII | |
|---|---|---|---|---|---|---|---|---|---|---|---|---|---|
| No. | % | No. | % | No. | % | No. | % | No. | % | No. | % | No. | % |
| 1 | (5·9) | 1 | (10·0) | 4 | (44·4) | 2 | (11·8) | 9 | (23·7) | 2 | (9·5) | 2 | (9·5) |
| 7 | (41·2) | 3 | (30·0) | 6 | (66·7) | 8 | (47·1) | 18 | (47·4) | 9 | (42·9) | 5 | (23·8) |
| 2 | (11·8) | 1 | (10·0) | 1 | (11·1) | 4 | (23·5) | 4 | (10·5) | 4 | (19·0) | 3 | (14·3) |
| 2 | (11·8) | — | ( ) | 3 | (33·3) | 4 | (23·5) | 11 | (28·9) | 6 | (28·6) | 6 | (28·6) |
| — | ( ) | — | ( ) | 1 | (11·1) | 3 | (17·6) | 5 | (13·2) | 3 | (14·3) | 3 | (14·3) |
| 3 | (17·6) | 2 | (20·0) | 1 | (11·1) | 6 | (35·3) | 9 | (23·7) | 5 | (23·8) | 5 | (23·8) |
| 5 | (29·4) | 2 | (20·0) | 7 | (77·8) | 11 | (64·7) | 24 | (63·2) | 13 | (61·9) | 7 | (33·3) |
| 2 | (11·8) | 2 | (20·0) | 3 | (33·3) | 9 | (52·9) | 13 | (34·2) | 12 | (57·1) | 7 | (33·3) |
| — | ( ) | — | ( ) | — | ( ) | 2 | (11·8) | 3 | (7·9) | 2 | (9·5) | 3 | (14·3) |
| 8 | (47·1) | 5 | (50·0) | 6 | (66·7) | 13 | (76·5) | 24 | (63·2) | 12 | (57·1) | 13 | (61·9) |
| | | | | | | | | | | | | | |
| 9 | (52·9) | 5 | (50·0) | 8 | (88·9) | 12 | (70·6) | 27 | (71·1) | 13 | (61·9) | 13 | (61·9) |
| 8 | (47·1) | 5 | (50·0) | 6 | (66·7) | 8 | (47·1) | 15 | (39·5) | 9 | (42·9) | 12 | (57·1) |
| 6 | (35·3) | 4 | (40·0) | 5 | (55·6) | 11 | (64·7) | 17 | (44·7) | 8 | (38·1) | 8 | (38·1) |
| 5 | (29·4) | 3 | (30·0) | 4 | (44·4) | 7 | (41·2) | 7 | (18·4) | 6 | (28·6) | 8 | (38·1) |
| 5 | (29·4) | 2 | (20·0) | 5 | (55·6) | 9 | (52·9) | 16 | (42·1) | 9 | (42·9) | 5 | (23·8) |
| 4 | (23·5) | 1 | (10·0) | 1 | (11·1) | 9 | (52·9) | 14 | (36·8) | 6 | (28·6) | 7 | (33·3) |
| 4 | (23·5) | 1 | (10·0) | 1 | (11·1) | 4 | (23·5) | 4 | (10·5) | 3 | (14·3) | 4 | (19·0) |
| 1 | (5·9) | — | ( ) | 1 | (11·1) | 3 | (17·6) | 4 | (10·5) | 1 | (4·8) | 3 | (14·3) |
| 5 | (29·4) | 1 | (10·0) | — | ( ) | 9 | (52·9) | 8 | (21·1) | 8 | (38·1) | 9 | (42·9) |
| 7 | (41·2) | 3 | (30·0) | 6 | (66·7) | 9 | (52·9) | 16 | (42·1) | 6 | (28·6) | 11 | (52·4) |
| 4 | (23·5) | 5 | (50·0) | 1 | (11·1) | 8 | (47·1) | 6 | (15·8) | 5 | (23·8) | 6 | (28·6) |
| 4 | (23·5) | 3 | (30·0) | 2 | (22·2) | 5 | (29·4) | 8 | (21·1) | 3 | (14·3) | 4 | (19·0) |
| 1 | (5·9) | — | ( ) | 1 | (11·1) | 2 | (11·8) | 4 | (10·5) | 3 | (14·3) | 2 | (9·5) |
| 7 | (41·2) | 5 | (50·0) | 8 | (88·9) | 9 | (52·9) | 22 | (57·9) | 10 | (47·6) | 10 | (47·6) |
| 5 | (29·4) | 4 | (40·0) | 4 | (44·4) | 5 | (29·4) | 9 | (23·7) | 2 | (9·5) | 5 | (23·8) |
| 1 | (5·9) | — | ( ) | — | ( ) | 3 | (17·6) | 1 | (2·6) | — | ( ) | 1 | (4·8) |
| — | ( ) | 1 | (10·0) | 4 | (44·4) | 1 | (5·9) | 3 | (7·9) | 1 | (4·8) | 2 | (9·5) |
| 2 | (11·8) | 1 | (10·0) | — | ( ) | 1 | (5·9) | 2 | (5·3) | 1 | (4·8) | — | ( ) |
| 2 | (11·8) | 2 | (20·0) | 1 | (11·1) | 3 | (17·6) | 2 | (5·3) | 1 | (4·8) | — | ( ) |
| — | ( ) | — | ( ) | — | ( ) | 1 | (5·9) | 2 | (5·3) | — | ( ) | — | ( ) |
| — | ( ) | — | ( ) | — | ( ) | — | ( ) | 1 | (2·6) | — | ( ) | — | ( ) |
| — | ( ) | — | ( ) | — | ( ) | 4 | (23·5) | 2 | (5·3) | 2 | (9·5) | — | ( ) |
| 17 | | 10 | | 9 | | 17 | | 38 | | 21 | | 21 | |

differences

### TABLE 9.10
#### RELATIONSHIP BETWEEN SEX OF PARENT WITH CHRONIC OR RECURRENT PHYSICAL ILLNESS AND SEX OF CHILD

| Sex of affected child | Sex of parent | | | Total No. |
|---|---|---|---|---|
| | Both ill No. % | Father only ill No. % | Mother only ill No. % | |
| Male | 16 (69·6) | 48 (63·2) | 60 (65·9) | 124 |
| Female | 7 (30·4) | 28 (36·8) | 31 (34·1) | 66 |
| Total | 23 | 76 | 91 | 190 |

TABLE 9.7

SYMPTOMS OF PARENT AND FIELDS OF DISORDER IN THE CHILD

Symptoms of Parent (key below)

| Field of Disorder (in the child) | I | | II | | III | | IV | | V | | VI | | VII | | VIII | | IX | | X | | XI | | XII | |
|---|---|---|---|---|---|---|---|---|---|---|---|---|---|---|---|---|---|---|---|---|---|---|---|---|
| | No. | % | No. | % | No. | % | No. | % | No. | % | No. | % | No. | % | No. | % | No. | % | No. | % | No. | % | No. | % |
| Primary habits | 52 | (81·3) | 56 | (75·7) | 28 | (80·0) | 32 | (76·2) | 7 | (53·8) | 10 | (58·8) | 5 | (50·0) | 8 | (88·9) | 13 | (76·5) | 29 | (76·3) | 16 | (76·2) | 12 | (57·1) |
| Secondary habits | 41 | (64·0) | 51 | (68·9) | 27 | (77·1) | 29 | (69·0) | 8 | (61·5) | 7 | (41·2) | 3 | (30·0) | 7 | (77·8) | 12 | (70·6) | 26 | (68·4) | 16 | (76·2) | 9 | (42·9) |
| Motor | 27 | (42·2) | 29 | (39·2) | 15 | (42·9) | 17 | (40·5) | 6 | (46·2) | 2 | (11·8) | 2 | (20·0) | 3 | (33·3) | 11 | (64·7) | 15 | (39·5) | 9 | (42·9) | 8 | (38·1) |
| Personal relationships | 60 | (93·8) | 67 | (90·5) | 34 | (97·1) | 39 | (92·9) | 11 | (84·6) | 15 | (88·2) | 9 | (90·0) | 9 | (100·0) | 16 | (94·1) | 36 | (94·7) | 19 | (90·5) | 20 | (95·2) |
| School/Work | 31 | (48·4) | 34 | (45·9) | 14 | (40·0) | 20 | (47·6) | 3 | (23·1) | 5 | (29·4) | 2 | (20·0) | 5 | (55·6) | 9 | (52·9) | 16 | (42·1) | 9 | (42·9) | 5 | (23·8) |
| Conduct | 44 | (68·8) | 49 | (66·2) | 26 | (74·3) | 32 | (76·2) | 12 | (92·3) | 11 | (64·7) | 7 | (70·0) | 7 | (77·8) | 14 | (82·4) | 24 | (63·2) | 13 | (61·9) | 18 | (85·7) |
| Psychic | 37 | (57·8) | 42 | (56·8) | 24 | (68·6) | 26 | (61·9) | 7 | (53·8) | 10 | (58·8) | 7 | (70·0) | 8 | (88·9) | 14 | (82·4) | 25 | (65·8) | 12 | (57·1) | 13 | (61·9) |
| Somatic | 11 | (17·2) | 14 | (18·9) | 7 | (20·0) | 7 | (16·7) | — | | 3 | (17·6) | 2 | (20·0) | 1 | (11·1) | 4 | (23·5) | 5 | (13·2) | 2 | (9·5) | — | |
| Allergic | 6 | (9·4) | 6 | (8·1) | 1 | (2·9) | 4 | (9·5) | — | | — | | — | | — | | 4 | (23·5) | 2 | (5·3) | 2 | (9·5) | — | |
| Total | 64 | | 74 | | 35 | | 42 | | 13 | | 17 | | 10 | | 9 | | 17 | | 38 | | 21 | | 21 | |

No significant differences

KEY:

| | | | |
|---|---|---|---|
| I | Anxiety | VII | Hallucinations |
| II | Depression | VIII | Obsessional symptoms |
| III | Disturbed relationship Spouse | IX | Hysterical symptoms |
| IV | Disturbed relationship Child | X | Somatic symptoms |
| V | Disturbed relationship Others | XI | Suicidal acts or gestures |
| VI | Delusions | XII | Other symptoms |

# INDEX OF AUTHORS

# INDEX OF SUBJECTS

PRINTED IN GREAT BRITAIN BY
THE CAMELOT PRESS LIMITED
LONDON AND SOUTHAMPTON